Sampling Inspection by Variables

SAMPLING INSPECTION
BY VARIABLES

Albert H. Bowker

Associate Professor of Statistics
Stanford University

Henry P. Goode

Associate Professor of Mechanical Engineering
Stanford University

FIRST EDITION

New York   Toronto   London
McGRAW-HILL BOOK COMPANY, INC.
1952

SAMPLING INSPECTION BY VARIABLES

Library of Congress Catalog Card Number: 51-12589

THE MAPLE PRESS COMPANY, YORK, PA.

To Gladys

PREFACE

The major purpose of this book is to present a set of variables sampling inspection plans for use in an integrated inspection program. The idea of publishing such a set of plans was under consideration at the Statistical Research Group at Columbia University at the time a set of attribute plans was constructed. The Statistical Research Group disbanded on September 30, 1945, before it was possible to prepare variables tables. The Office of Naval Research, however, undertook in 1948 to support the preparation of such tables at Stanford University and the present work is based entirely on material developed by the project. The SRG attribute tables were published in 1948 in *Sampling Inspection*, edited by Freeman, Friedman, Mosteller, and Wallis. The general organization of this book parallels that of *Sampling Inspection*, to which readers are referred for a more detailed discussion of the nature of sampling inspection and of the steps in the installation of sampling plans, which are the same for both variables and attribute inspection. The authors have attempted, however, to make this book essentially complete, and a short discussion has been included of all the steps involved in setting up a sampling inspection plan.

The core of the book is the set of variables tables and their operating characteristic curves. The tables may be used as part of a systematic inspection scheme as described in the book, involving an arbitrary relation between lot size, sample size, and classification of plans by the 95% point of the operating characteristic curve, or, alternatively, as a catalogue of plans from which a selection may be made in other ways.

The authors have benefited from discussions with many of their colleagues and with statisticians in government and industrial concerns. Particular thanks are extended to Profs. L. E. Moses and Herman Rubin for the assistance on the procedures for two-sided plans developed in Chap. 11, Prof. Lawrance Bell for his preparation of a form for computations and Prof. E. L. Grant for his helpful comments. We are especially grateful to Dr. Herbert Solomon of the Office of Naval Research for his continuing support and numerous helpful suggestions. The authors are deeply indebted to Mrs. Gladys Garabedian, who undertook a large part of the responsibility for the preparation of the tables, as well as assisting with editorial work. The authors are also indebted to Mrs. Joyce Shore for editorial help.

STANFORD, CALIF.   ALBERT H. BOWKER

January, 1952   HENRY P. GOODE

CONTENTS

Preface vi

Chapter 1. INTRODUCTION 1

1. Purpose of This Book 1
2. Measures of Quality 2
3. Scope of the Plans 3
4. Selection and Operation of a Variables Plan 4
5. The Field for Variables Sampling 4
6. Relation of Variables Plans to Attribute Plans 6
7. Variables Sampling When the Product Standard Deviation Is Known . . 7

Chapter 2. GENERAL PRINCIPLES OF SAMPLING INSPECTION BY VARIABLES 9

1. Objectives of Acceptance Inspection 9
2. Methods of Acceptance Inspection 9
3. Objectives in Lot-by-lot Sampling Inspection 10
4. Risks in Lot-by-lot Sampling Inspection 11
5. Examples of Variables Plans 11
6. Mathematical Basis of Variables Acceptance Plans 13
7. The Assumption of a Normal Distribution 18

Chapter 3. PROPERTIES OF THE VARIABLES PLANS 25

1. The Operating Characteristic Curve 25
2. Classification of Sampling Plans; AQL and LTPD 26
3. Disposition of Rejected Inspection Lots and Its Effect on the Quality of the Accepted Product; AOQ and AOQL 29
4. Savings in Inspection of Variables Plans over Attribute Plans . . . 32
5. The Choice between Single Sampling and Double Sampling 33
6. Comparison of Sequential Sampling by Attributes with Sampling by Variables 34
7. Prescribed Sample Sizes 36
8. The Inspection Level 38
9. Reduced and Tightened Inspection 38

Chapter 4. INSTALLATION OF THE VARIABLES PLANS 40

1. Determination of What an Item of Product Should Be 40
2. Listing of Defects for Which the Item Is to Be Inspected 40
3. Selection of an Acceptable Quality Level (AQL) for Each Defect . . 41
4. Selection of an Inspection Level 43
5. Determination of the Size of the Inspection Lot 45
6. Determination of the Sample-size Letter 46
7. The Choice between Single and Double Sampling 47
8. Determination of the Specific Plan to Apply 48
9. Responsibility for the Installation of Plans 50

Chapter 5.   OPERATION OF THE VARIABLES PLANS   52
 1. Formation of Inspection Lots.   52
 2. Drawing of Samples   52
 3. Inspection of Items in the Sample   54
 4. Calculation to Determine Disposal of the Lot   54
 5. Optional Forms for the Criteria   59
 6. Computation of Process Averages   60
 7. Determination of Whether Tightened or Reduced Inspection Should Be
    Applied   64
 8. Tightened Inspection   65
 9. Reduced Inspection.   67
10. Selection and Operation of Plans in Terms of the AOQL   68
11. Curtailed Inspection   69
12. Combined Variables and Attribute Plans   69

Chapter 6.   PLANS FOR USE WHEN THE STANDARD DEVIATION
             OF THE PRODUCT IS KNOWN.   72
 1. Field of Use for These Plans   72
 2. Savings in the Use of Known-sigma Plans   73
 3. Determination of the Product Standard Deviation.   74
 4. Known-sigma Plans   75
 5. Installation and Operation of the Plans.   77
 6. Tightened and Reduced Inspection   79

Chapter 7.   PROCEDURES FOR TWO-SIDED SPECIFICATION LIMITS   80
 1. The Field for Two-sided Plans   80
 2. Two-sided Plans for Use Where the Standard Deviation Is Known. . .   80
 3. Two-sided Plans for Use Where the Standard Deviation Is Not Known .   82
 4. The Use of Different AQL Classes for Each of the Limits   84

Chapter 8.   ILLUSTRATIVE APPLICATIONS   86
 1. A Single-sampling Plan and a Single-sided Specification Limit   86
 2. A Double-sampling Plan and a Single-sided Specification Limit   93

Chapter 9.   THE USE OF CONTROL CHARTS IN SAMPLING INSPEC-
             TION   97
 1. Meaning of Control   97
 2. The Control Chart in Acceptance Inspection   98
 3. Control Limits for the Means of Samples 103
 4. Control Limits for the Standard Deviations of Samples 106
 5. The Coefficient of Displacement 109

Chapter 10.   CONSTRUCTION OF SAMPLING PLANS AND STAND-
              ARD PROCEDURE. 114
 1. Description of Standard Attribute Procedure 114
 2. Construction of Parallel Variables Plans. 115
 3. Construction of Single-sampling Variables Plans and the Match between the
    Attribute and Variables Plans 117
 4. Construction of Double-sampling Plans. 121
 5. Sequential Methods 122
 6. Adjustment of Sampling Plans 122

Chapter 11. THE MATHEMATICS OF SAMPLING INSPECTION BY VARIABLES 125
1. Single-sampling Plans 125
2. Double-sampling Plans 127
3. Two-sided Tests 133
4. Combined Variables and Attribute Plans 140

Appendix. COMPUTING TECHNIQUES AND METHODS OF APPLYING THE ACCEPTANCE CRITERIA 143
1. Computation of Σx and Σx^2 143
2. The Standard Method 146
3. Inspection and Computation Forms 148
4. An Optional Form for the Standard Criteria 148
5. The Difference Method 150
6. The Quadratic Method—Analytical Solution 151
7. The Quadratic Method—Graphical Solution 153
8. The Squared-difference Method—Analytical Solution 155
9. The Squared-difference Method—Graphical Solution 156

List of Symbols 157

TABLES AND CHARTS 163
A. Sample-size Letter, by Inspection Level and Size of Inspection Lot . . . 164
B. Summary of Single-sampling Variables Plans, Classified by Acceptable Quality Level and Sample-size Letter 165
C. Summary of Double-sampling Variables Plans, Classified by Acceptable Quality Level and Sample-size Letter 166
D. Acceptable Quality Level (AQL) and Lot Tolerance Percent Defective (LTPD) of Single- and Double-sampling Variables Plans 168
E. Single- and Double-sampling Plans and Operating-characteristic Curves, Classified by Sample-size Letter, Acceptable Quality Level, and Average Outgoing-quality Limit 169
F. Constants for the Optional Single-sampling Acceptance Criterion . . . 190
G. Estimated Process Average as a Function of $\bar{k}$ 192
H. Upper and Lower Limits on Process Average 194
I. Sample-size Letters for Average Outgoing-quality Limit (AOQL) Classes and Acceptable Quality Level (AQL) Classes 196
J. Factors for Control Chart Limits 197
K. Summary of Single-sampling Variables Plans for Known Sigma, Classified by Acceptable Quality Level and Sample-size Letter 199
L. Summary of Double-sampling Variables Plans for Known Sigma, Classified by Acceptable Quality Level and Sample-size Letter 200
M. Comparison of AQL and LTPD for Single-sampling, Known-sigma and Unknown-sigma Plans 202
N. Upper and Lower Limits on Process Average for Known-sigma Plans . . 202
O. Nomograph to Determine $P(A_2)$ 205
P. Table of Points for Constructing Acceptance Regions for Two-sided Specification Limits 206

Index 211

CHAPTER 1

INTRODUCTION

1. PURPOSE OF THIS BOOK

This book has been written to present a set of plans for sampling inspection where item quality is expressed on a variables basis; that is, the item characteristic being inspected is measured and the reading recorded, as opposed to inspection on an attribute basis, which simply classifies an item as defective or non-defective. The principles of attribute inspection along with tables and procedures for their use have been presented in "Sampling Inspection,"† whose general structure the present book follows.

For many applications, plans based on variables are superior to those based on attributes, particularly as a means of reducing the over-all sampling inspection costs. The plans are presented as part of a standard variables sampling procedure which may be applied to many different products but may be used as a catalogue of plans by those who construct tailor-made procedures.

Standard procedures for the selection, installation, and operation of variables plans are presented. To assist in a more complete understanding of the plans and their use, elementary principles of sampling inspection are discussed, particularly when inspection is by variables. Finally, two chapters are included for the reader with a more theoretical interest: Chap. 10 discusses the disposition of some of the problems that arose during the preparation of the plans and Chap. 11 presents the mathematical theory behind the plans.

In general, these sampling plans and the procedures for their use have been developed for the needs of acceptance inspection of raw materials, semi-finished parts, or completed products. They can also be used for sampling inspection of outgoing product or for sampling inspection of goods-in-process within a plant, to determine at a given point the acceptability of the product for use in succeeding operations.

Since it is likely that most readers will be familiar with the existing sampling techniques employed in attribute inspection, either through

† Statistical Research Group, Columbia University, "Sampling Inspection: Principles, Procedures and Tables for Single, Double, and Sequential Sampling in Acceptance Inspection and Quality Control," McGraw-Hill Book Company, Inc., New York, 1948.

1

practice or through the extensive literature in this field, many items common to both attribute and variables plans, such as the procedure for selecting a sample, will not be treated in any great detail. However, the discussion is intended to be complete enough to enable installations to be made without reference to other plans or material.

2. MEASURES OF QUALITY

In acceptance inspection, and in much other sampling inspection, one is concerned with two aspects of quality: first, that of determining the quality of an individual item or unit of product, and second, that of determining the over-all quality of a lot, where a lot is a given group of individual items of product.

In evaluating and describing the quality of an item, one of the following general types of inspection will be used, the choice depending on the characteristic being measured and on the device or method most appropriate for making such measurements:

a. Variables Inspection. In evaluating the quality of an item on a variables basis, the characteristic in question is measured along a continuous scale in terms of milligrams, pounds, inches, volts, seconds, or some such unit.

b. Attribute Inspection. Under attribute inspection of an item, the characteristic in question is observed or checked with an indicating device (or in some cases a measuring device) and simply classified as either satisfactory or unsatisfactory. Use of go and not-go gauges for checking dimensional properties of parts is a widely used method of attribute inspection.

c. Counting Defects per Unit. For certain products quality characteristics of the item are evaluated by counting the number of a given type of defect in an item. For example, one measure of the quality of enamel insulation on copper wire is the number of "pinholes" or bare spots in a specified number of linear feet of wire.

The quality of a lot, on the other hand, will be described in other terms. Some of the most common measures are listed below. The choice among these will depend on the nature of the product and on its ultimate use. Where sampling inspection is to be used, the choice may depend on the nature of the sampling procedures that are available.

a. Percentage Defective. The percentage of defective items in the lot is the method most commonly used in describing lot quality and is the basis on which most sampling plans have been constructed.

b. The Average Number of Defects per Item of Product. Ordinarily, in this case, item quality is measured by counting the defects per unit for each item.

c. The Arithmetic Mean of Item Qualities in the Lot. This assumes that quality may be represented in the lot by a numerical value.

d. The Standard Deviation of Item Qualities in the Lot. The standard deviation is a measure of the amount of variation of the quality characteristic from item to item.

Sampling inspection in general may take one of two forms:

a. Lot-by-lot. Under this method, product coming from a process or a plant is grouped into lots containing a definite number of items. A sample is taken from each lot and the items inspected; on the basis of what is found in the sample, the lot is either accepted or held for screening or other disposition. Thus, discrete groups of products are put to a test and accepted or rejected as separate entities.

b. Continuous. Under this method, product is not grouped into discrete lots. Items for inspection are taken directly from the flow of a product as it leaves a processing station or assembly line or as it enters another department or plant. The desired outgoing quality is maintained by switching from sampling inspection of the product flow to screening inspection when the sampling indicates deterioration of the quality level.

3. SCOPE OF THE PLANS

The sampling plans presented here are for use where inspection of the sample items is by variables. This makes them readily available for a great many installations. Tests of materials for strength and other similar mechanical properties and tests for weight, for electrical characteristics, for chemical properties, as well as many inspections of dimension, are on a variables basis.

For these plans, lot quality is judged in terms of the percentage of items that are defective. Variables data from a sample may be used readily to make decisions when lot quality is specified in terms of the mean and standard deviation. However, the percent defective basis seems preferable, since the percent defective is the measure used under the existing attribute plans and since it has been customary in industry for lot quality to be described in this way. Finally, these plans are for use only with lot-by-lot inspection.

In summary: Item inspection is by variables; lot quality is judged in terms of percent defective; and acceptance is lot-by-lot.

For this field of use, plans are presented that are based on both the drawing of single samples and the drawing of double samples from the inspection lot. Sequential plans, in which more than two samples may be drawn, are not included (see Chap. 10, Sec. 5). Detailed plans are given for use with quality characteristics having a single limit—either a maximum value or a minimum value.   Methods are given for using these plans for characteristics for which both a maximum value and a minimum value are specified.

4. SELECTION AND OPERATION OF A VARIABLES PLAN

The intent of this book has been to include a fairly complete set of plans, so that a suitable one is available for almost any industrial or governmental use.   To make a proper choice among them, consideration must be given (presumably by inspection executives) to the quality, in terms of percent defective, one is willing to accept and to the risk one is willing to assume that some lots of a higher percent defective may be accepted.   After decisions are made on these matters, the inspection supervisor, following a prescribed procedure, can easily select an appropriate plan.

The operation of the plan selected for a particular product involves the following steps [since this outline is given only as a background for the discussion to follow, a single-sampling plan and a one-sided specification limit are assumed; there is some variation in steps (b), (e), and (f) if a double-sampling plan is employed or if a two-sided specification limit must be met]:

(a) The product is grouped into inspection lots.

(b) A sample of prescribed size is drawn from each lot.

(c) Each item in the sample is inspected (by measurement) to ascertain its quality x.

(d) The mean $\bar{x}$ and standard deviation s of the measurements are computed for each sample.

(e) The sample standard deviation s is multiplied by a constant k which is specified by the selected plan.

(f) If the specification is an upper limit, the sum of the sample mean and the modified sample standard deviation, $\bar{x} + ks$, is compared with the specification limit U for the item.   (If the specification is a lower limit L, $\bar{x} - ks$ is compared with L.)

(g) On the basis of the comparison in step (f), each lot is either accepted or rejected.

5. THE FIELD FOR VARIABLES SAMPLING

The important advantage of sampling inspection by variables over sampling inspection by attributes is that, for any desired degree of protection, fewer items have to be inspected to judge the acceptability of a lot.   For example, if it is necessary to inspect a sample of 75 items under an attribute inspection plan to secure a certain degree of protection, under a variables plan a sample of only 35 items would have to be inspected to get the same degree of protection. This advantage may also be expressed by saying that, for samples of the same size, inspection by variables gives a smaller risk of accepting lots of unacceptable quality than inspection by attributes.

It is obvious that the measurement of an item under variables inspection gives much more information about that item than inspection on a go and not-go basis. For example, if we measure the resistance of an electrical part and find it to be 1,780 ohms, we know much more about the quality of this particular item than we do if we learn only that its resistance falls below a specified maximum value.

Since variables inspection of each item gives much more information about the quality of the item, variables inspection of all items in a sample yields more information about the quality of the lot than attribute inspection. This advantage is realized in a practical way through reduced sample sizes. Actual savings in numbers of items inspected will be shown in some detail in the next chapter. Hence, variables plans should be considered when inspection of the item is costly. If inspection of an item requires a great deal of inspection labor, if expensive equipment and personnel are occupied in the test, or if the item is damaged or destroyed by the test, use of variables plans will be found profitable.

Another advantage of variables inspection for acceptance sampling is that data is provided for the most useful forms of control charts—control charts for the average and control charts for the standard deviation. With the information provided by the sample data and by the control charts the receiver is able to give the supplier detailed and specific information that may assist him in improving his manufacturing processes. One of the principal purposes of acceptance inspection is to induce the supplier to improve the quality of his product when necessary so that better product will be submitted in the future. The diagnostic information that will be given the supplier may be a very useful by-product of variables inspection.

A minor advantage of variables inspection for acceptance sampling is that borderline items in the sample present no problem to the inspector. Under attribute inspection his decision as to whether some particular borderline item is defective or not will often decide the disposal of the lot; hence a decision is difficult to make. Under variables inspection, he has no such decision to make; he merely records what he reads. It makes little difference in the disposal of the lot if his reading is just under the specification limit, at the limit, or just above it. For this reason also, personal bias through giving borderline items "the benefit of the doubt" is practically impossible.

Variables plans have a number of disadvantages which limit their use in favor of attribute plans for many applications.   Foremost among them is that for many products variables inspection of a quality characteristic often requires more inspection skill and time, more complicated tools and in other ways is more costly than an attribute inspection method that may be available.   Under such circumstances, it may be found preferable to use the attribute method, even though a sample consisting of more items must be inspected.

A second disadvantage is that more record keeping and more arithmetic are needed after data is obtained from the sample in order to determine whether or not to accept the lot.   The clerical steps are not as much work in actual practice as one may be led to believe by reading a description of them.   A graphical method to replace computational steps (d), (e), and (f), as listed in Sec. 4 above, may be used for products received in large volumes.   While this alternative requires more initial work on the part of the person installing the plan, it greatly reduces the calculations that have to be made by the inspector in routine operation.

Finally, plans based on variables call for more stringent mathematical assumptions; their selection and installation may call for considerably more ability and care on the part of those administering the sampling inspection program.   In particular, the plans are based on the assumption that distribution of item qualities follows the so-called "normal law." While very little is really known regarding the natural distribution of qualities, the indications are that the qualities of perhaps most of our industrial products do approximate closely enough a normal distribution. However, the administrator should be able to recognize the unusual circumstances under which the distribution of item quality is not approximately "normal."

In cases where items can be inspected on either a variables basis or an attribute basis, the choice between a variables sampling inspection plan and an attribute inspection plan is thus largely economic.   The one that has the lowest total costs, including inspection, clerical, and administrative expenses, should be used.   Both types of plans judge lot quality by what is usually the most appropriate measure—the percent defective. Choice of a plan of one type or the other will not, as will be shown in the next section, have any effect on acceptance standards.

6. RELATION OF VARIABLES PLANS TO ATTRIBUTE PLANS

Attribute sampling plans based on sound mathematical theory have become well established, having been used successfully by industry and government for a number of years.   The basic concepts were developed in the pioneering work in this field at the Bell Telephone Laboratories.†

Inasmuch as these variables plans are alternatives to existing attribute plans, it seemed advisable to design them as far as possible on a parallel basis.   Accordingly, their operating characteristic curves have been made to match quite closely the most recently published set of attribute plans, those developed for the Navy by the Columbia University Statistical Research Group and published in "Sampling Inspection." Fortunately, the mathematical procedures used to develop these variables plans made it possible to give them any desired operating properties and thus achieve this close match.   The extent of the matching will be discussed in Chap. 10.

Providing these two types of plans on a parallel basis makes possible their joint use in acceptance inspection, using one type or the other for any given item, the choice depending on which one gives the lowest total inspection costs.   Inspection executives, who are responsible for establishing standards for the acceptance of product, can do so without regard for the type of sampling plan that will be used.   Those responsible for the installation and operation of sampling procedures can choose either type with the assurance that this choice will not affect the desired protection.

7. VARIABLES SAMPLING WHEN THE PRODUCT STANDARD DEVIATION IS KNOWN

The most general type of variables sampling plans assume that for the item qualities to be tested both the mean (or average) and the standard deviation (or dispersion of the measurements about their mean value) are unknown.   Such plans could be used for products for which the standard deviation is known, but plans which use this known standard deviation explicitly will require smaller samples.   Although the basic or standard plans have been designed for the more important case of unknown standard deviation and the discussion in most of the text is written in these terms, in actual industrial practice the standard deviation of item measurements for many products is found to be constant from lot to lot and therefore can be determined prior to applying acceptance inspection.   For such products, alternative plans have been designed paralleling the unknown standard deviation plans.   The sample sizes associated with the known standard deviation plans are considerably

---

† The basic articles by H. F. Dodge and H. G. Romig published in the *Bell System Technical Journal* have been collected and republished in one volume.   See Harold F. Dodge and Harry G. Romig, "Sampling Inspection Tables: Single and Double Sampling," John Wiley & Sons, Inc., New York, 1944.

smaller than for the basic unknown standard deviation plans, and the computations required to determine the disposal of a lot are simplified. Hence, these plans, although presented as alternatives, should be considered as standard for the wide variety of products to which they may be applied.   When they are so considered, the unknown standard deviation plans will then be reserved for products whose standard deviation can be expected to vary from lot to lot and for products whose quality history is not known.   For these latter products, data from the initial lots can be used to determine whether or not the standard deviation is reasonably constant, and if it is so, an accurate estimate of its value can be determined.   If the initial data shows that the standard deviation is constant, then a change can be made to a parallel known standard deviation plan. A discussion of plans for products whose standard deviation is known, together with procedures for their selection and use, is given in Chap. 6. Methods of determining whether or not this type of plan may be used for a product are also outlined.   One step in a standard procedure for acceptance inspection should be to determine, when variables sampling is in use and sufficient quality history of a product is accumulated, whether or not plans based on a known standard deviation may be used.

Another alternative to the variables plans presented in this book is a procedure making use of both variables and attribute data.   Under this procedure, a sample is drawn and inspected on a variables basis.   If the action indicated is acceptance, the lot is accepted, but if the action indicated is rejection, an additional sample is drawn.   This additional sample is inspected on an attribute basis, and the final decision concerning the disposal of the lot is made on the basis of the attribute plan.   This alternative is appropriate when there is a chance that the lot has been screened by the supplier before submitting it to acceptance inspection.

CHAPTER 2

GENERAL PRINCIPLES OF SAMPLING INSPECTION BY VARIABLES

1. OBJECTIVES OF ACCEPTANCE INSPECTION

When a business establishment or government agency purchases raw materials, parts, or finished products, the purchase contract will often indicate that acceptance of the product is subject to having each item meet certain quality specifications. Similarly, in the transfer of goods-in-process or of finished parts among divisions of a particular organization, established quality standards for individual items must be met.

Both parties to such transfers realize that, if the product is made by mass-production methods, some of the items transferred will not meet the specifications. Furthermore, the number and location of these defectives in any lot, shipment, or order will rarely be known. To protect the purchaser against the acceptance of an undue quantity of defective items, to exert pressure on the vendor to improve his product when necessary, and to assist in quality control and in the reduction of production costs when the product is transferred within an organization—to ensure these objectives, some form of acceptance inspection has been found desirable.

2. METHODS OF ACCEPTANCE INSPECTION

Acceptance inspection usually takes one of the three following forms:

a. Screening. Under this method all the submitted items are individually inspected and individually accepted or rejected. This procedure is used when elimination of defectives is essential. Ordinarily, however, screening is not feasible; the cost of inspecting each item may be too high, or the necessary tests may damage or destroy the item. In addition, screening cannot guarantee the removal of all defective items. It is impossible for inspectors to work with 100 percent accuracy, especially when large numbers of items are inspected and defective items are not particularly obvious. In some cases, sampling inspection with its lower costs may be able to give the same quality assurance.

b. Control Charts. Under certain circumstances the receiver can run control charts on submitted products or can obtain copies of charts maintained by the supplier at various stages in his production processes. Because they supply useful information about the quality level of the product and about the degree of control at the various production processes used in its manufacture, these charts can be of great value to an acceptance program. The use of control charts in acceptance inspection is discussed in Chap. 9.

c. *Lot-by-lot Sampling Inspection.* For most applications experience has shown this to be the most satisfactory method of acceptance inspection. If statistically sound sampling plans are used, any desired degree of protection can be obtained.

3. OBJECTIVES IN LOT-BY-LOT SAMPLING INSPECTION

In sampling inspection it is assumed that the submitted product is or can be divided or combined into physically distinct lots. The further assumption is made that some variation in the percentage of defective items from lot to lot is inherent in the nature of the manufacturing process.

A sample, or two samples under some plans, of relatively few items is taken from a lot and inspected. The inspection lot as a whole is then accepted or rejected on the basis of data obtained from examining the items in the sample.

Under properly constructed sampling plans a large proportion of the better quality lots will be accepted and a large proportion of the low-quality lots will be rejected. The rejected lots are returned to the plant of either the supplier or the receiver for disposal elsewhere or for screening in order to be resubmitted. In the accepted lots the average percentage of defective items will be less than the average percentage of defectives in all the lots originally submitted.

Lot-by-lot sampling inspection improves the quality of the accepted product in several ways. In the first place, inspection by lots lowers the number of defective items per accepted lot as compared with the number of defectives in the lots taken as a whole. Second, the rejection and return to the supplier of certain lots for screening, rework, or scrap further improve quality; the larger the number of such rejected lots, the greater the costs incurred by the supplier, and consequently, the more the supplier will attempt to produce and submit lots of better quality in the future. Finally, the data obtained during sampling inspection, if properly interpreted and utilized, can be of considerable help to the supplier in his efforts to improve and control his production processes.

The terms "supplier" and "receiver," it should be noted, are used for purposes of clarification. Discussion of sampling inspection has often been in terms of a "vendor" who sells his product to a "purchaser." But sampling inspection is equally suitable for use in the transfer of goods between plants in a single company or between departments or operations in an individual plant. The "vendor" may be a given work station, department, or plant; the "purchaser," the work station or department which follows in the production process. To avoid possible confusion, we shall use the terms "supplier" and "receiver."

4. RISKS IN LOT-BY-LOT SAMPLING INSPECTION

No acceptance procedure based upon sampling can assure the acceptance of only good items. Under these variables plans, as under plans based upon attribute inspection, accepted inspection lots may contain some defective items. Another limitation of these plans as well as of the attribute plans is that they will permit occasionally the acceptance of an inspection lot with a relatively high percentage of defective items and the rejection of a lot containing a relatively low percentage of defectives. The element of chance cannot be avoided in the drawing of sample items from a lot, and consequently, the quality of the items in the sample may occasionally depart considerably from the quality of the items in the lot.

These risks may have to be assumed by the receiver for many of his purchases, because screening inspection costs too much, destroys the item, or does not guarantee anyway that all defective items will be detected and removed. Later we shall show how the receiver may choose his degree of risk.

5. EXAMPLES OF VARIABLES PLANS

Preparatory to the discussion in the rest of the chapter, a few examples of the operation of typical variables acceptance plans are given. For the sake of simplicity products have been chosen which have only one quality characteristic per item to be inspected and a single specification limit for that characteristic. Since the discussion is to cover the more general case in which the standard deviation of the product is not known, the examples illustrate unknown-sigma plans.

5.1. Example of a Plan Based upon Single Sampling

A small metal item is received in large quantities. For an item to be acceptable, its hardness must not exceed U, a specified Rockwell hardness number of 68 (30-N scale).

(a) In view of the function of this item and the conditions surrounding its manufacture and sale, the receiver decides that a sampling plan giving an acceptable quality level of 0.5 percent defective will be appropriate.

(b) The receiving inspector groups the product into inspection lots of 5,000 items. From each lot he selects at random a sample of 70 items.

(c) The items in the sample are tested for hardness, and a Rockwell hardness number x recorded for each.

(d) The mean $\bar{x}$ and the standard deviation s are calculated for the group of 70 readings obtained from the sample. (Procedures for calculating the mean and standard deviation will be presented later.) The standard deviation is multiplied by 2.132, a constant k given by the sampling plan used.

(e) The mean $\bar{x}$ and the modified standard deviation ks are added together. If their sum, $\bar{x} + ks$, is greater than U, the maximum allowable Rockwell hardness number of 68, the lot is rejected. If their sum is 68 or less, the lot is accepted.

The procedure (c) to (e) is repeated for each lot.

5.2. Example of a Plan Based upon Double Sampling

An electrical part is received in large quantities. To be satisfactory the resistance of the part must not fall below L, a specified minimum value of 1,100 ohms.

(a) After considering the probable quality of the submitted product and considering the consequences of accepting a defective part, the receiver decides that an acceptable level would be in the range 0.32 to 0.65 percent defective.

(b) The receiving inspector groups the incoming product into lots of 5,000 items. From each lot he selects at random a first sample of 30 items.

(c) Each item in the sample is tested to obtain its resistance x_1.

(d) The mean $\bar{x}_1$ and the standard deviation s_1 are calculated for the group of 30 readings taken from the items of this first sample.

(e) This standard deviation s_1 is multiplied by 2.373, a constant k_a determined by the sampling plan used. The product is subtracted from the mean $\bar{x}_1$.

(1) If the result is equal to or greater than L, the minimum allowable resistance of 1,100 ohms, the lot is accepted.

(2) If the lot is not accepted under the criterion in (1), the standard deviation s_1 is then multiplied by 1.762, a second constant k_r obtained from the selected sampling plan. This product is subtracted from the mean $\bar{x}_1$. If the result is equal to or less than 1,100, the lot is rejected.

(3) If the lot is neither accepted by the calculation using k_a nor rejected by the calculation using k_r, then a second sample must be drawn.

(f) The inspector takes from the lot a second sample of 60 items.

(g) The resistance of each part is measured and recorded.

(*h*) The readings obtained from this second sample are combined with the readings from the first sample, and the mean $\bar{x}_t$ and the standard deviation s_t are calculated for the combined sample now totaling 90 items.

(*i*) This standard deviation s_t is multiplied by 2.171, a third constant k_t obtained from the selected sampling plan. This product is subtracted from the mean $\bar{x}_t$. If the result is equal to or greater than 1,100, the lot is accepted. If the result is less than 1,100, the lot is rejected.

Procedures (*a*) to (*e*) are repeated for each lot. When a second sample is required, procedures (*f*) to (*i*) are also repeated.

6. MATHEMATICAL BASIS OF VARIABLES ACCEPTANCE PLANS

Additional insight into variables sampling procedures can be gained by considering an example in detail. The illustration in Sec. 5.1 which dealt with the problem of controlling the hardness of a product will be used.

6.1. Description of Distribution of Item Qualities

Let us assume that every item in the lot is tested, rather than sampled, and that the Rockwell hardness number is recorded for each. Then let us assume that the number of items having each Rockwell hardness number can be tabulated as follows:

Rockwell Hardness Reading	Number of Times Reading Occurred
55	1
56	17
57	135
58	503
59	1,110
60	1,470
61	1,120
62	490
63	125
64	26
65	3

Such a tabulation could be plotted as a histogram (Fig. 2.1) where the number of occurrences of each possible value is plotted on the vertical scale. This diagram shows the readings distributed symmetrically about a central value, the lot mean μ (the dashed line), with the values nearest the lot mean occurring most frequently.

If the production process had produced items with hardness readings more widely scattered, the distribution would be flatter. If it had produced items with hardness values more tightly clustered, the distribution would be higher and narrower. The most useful and most commonly accepted single measure of this variance of individual readings from the mean is the standard deviation. Tightly clustered values have a small standard deviation; for widely scattered values the standard deviation is relatively large. The production process might also produce a lot with items possessing a larger mean (average) hardness or a lot with a smaller mean than that indicated in Fig. 2.1.

These two statistical parameters, the mean and the standard deviation, together describe the distribution in a concise and useful manner. The

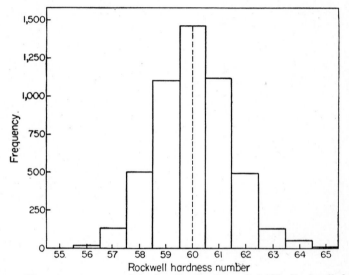

FIG. 2.1. Histogram representing the distribution of 5,000 Rockwell hardness readings.

mean μ is the expected value of the reading. The standard deviation σ provides a measure of the departure of individual readings from the mean. If the difference between any individual value and the mean is expressed as a fraction or a multiple of the standard deviation, it is possible to determine what proportion of the readings exceeds that value, provided the shape of this distribution is similar to a curve for which the mathematical formula is known.

6.2. Proportion Defective in Terms of Mean and Standard Deviation

Experience has shown that the normal curve, or Gaussian distribution, is so closely approximated by many of the distributions of measured quality characteristics that for purposes of acceptance inspection it is reasonable to assume the normality of these distributions. The Rockwell hardness test data in the example of Sec. 5.1 shown in Fig. 2.1 forms a distribution which for all practical purposes may be represented by a smooth bell-shaped curve of the true normal form. This normal curve (Fig. 2.2) has the same mean μ and standard deviation σ as the lot. The value U represents the specified tolerance limit—in this case, the maximum acceptable hardness test reading. The distance from μ to any value such as U may be expressed by the ratio of that distance $(U - \mu)$ to σ. Thus, we define $K = (U - \mu)/\sigma$, where K is the number of standard deviations from U to μ.

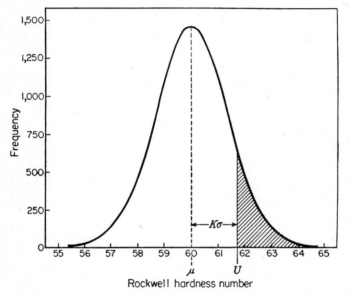

FIG. 2.2.   Normal curve fitted to the distribution of 5,000 Rockwell hardness readings.

The area under the normal curve (Fig. 2.2) represents the total number of items in the lot. The shaded area to the right of the value U represents the number of items in the lot that are defective. The proportion of items exceeding the limit U is the ratio of the shaded area to the total area. If μ and σ are known, the mathematical theory of the normal curve is such that it is possible to calculate precisely what proportion of the area under the normal curve lies beyond any given value U. For different values of K, tables giving the proportion of the area (that is, the number of items) beyond U are available. By substituting K for $\bar{k}$, Chart G can be used instead of the tables. For a normally distributed quality characteristic this chart shows the relationship between K and the proportion defective.

It should now be apparent that for any given specification limit the percentage of defective items in a lot will depend upon both the lot mean and the lot standard deviation. If the lot mean is given, the percent defective will be smaller with a smaller standard deviation and larger with a larger standard deviation. Similarly, if the standard deviation is given, the percent defective will be larger with a larger lot mean and smaller with a smaller lot mean. Therefore, the acceptability of a lot in terms of a suitable percent defective will depend upon the lot mean and the lot standard deviation.

If we were willing to accept lots with a percentage of defects less than a specified value, we could set a criterion for the acceptance of a lot whereby its mean plus the product of its standard deviation and K, where K is exceeded by the specified proportion defective, must be equal to or less than the upper specification limit U. This is expressed by the relation $\mu + K\sigma \leq U$. If the specification limit is a lower one L, $\mu - K\sigma$ must be equal to or greater than L. A criterion of this form is used in variables sampling inspection for items with one-sided specification limits.

6.3. Criterion for Acceptance When Decision Is Based upon a Sample

The discussion so far has been based upon the unrealistic assumption that the hardness readings of all the items in the lot are known. In sampling inspection the objective is to avoid inspecting all items and to judge the entire lot by the hardness readings of the relatively few items contained in a sample. Under variables sampling inspection plans the acceptance criterion has a similar form to that outlined above, except that the sample mean $\bar{x}$ and the sample standard deviation s are used in place of the lot mean μ and the lot standard deviation σ. Thus, the sum of the sample mean and the modified sample standard deviation is compared with the specification limit in order to determine whether or not the entire lot is acceptable. However, a different modifying factor k must be used in the calculation. The criterion for an upper limit would then be $\bar{x} + ks \leq U$, and for a lower limit, $\bar{x} - ks \geq L$.

This different factor k must be used when the mean and the standard deviation are derived from a sample of relatively few items, because the element of chance enters into the drawing of the sample items from the lot. It is unlikely that the quality of the sample will represent exactly the quality of the lot. By chance a sample may be drawn that contains a higher percentage of items with extreme hardness values than the actual percentage of such items in the lot; then again, the percentage of items with extreme hardness values may be lower. Thus, any given sample drawn from the lot can be expected to have a mean and a standard deviation differing from the mean and standard deviation of other samples picked from the same lot. However, if many samples were to be drawn from a given lot, the sample means would tend to cluster closely about the true lot mean and the sample standard deviations would tend to cluster about a value close to the lot standard deviation. Furthermore, if the sum $\bar{x} + ks$ were calculated for each sample, these sums would be grouped about a figure close to $\mu + K\sigma$, the criterion originally set up for judging the lot.

The effect of sampling error on this criterion can be expressed in mathematical terms, making it possible to determine a sample size and corresponding value for k that will give a sampling plan with any desired properties in terms of the probability of acceptance of lots of different quality. This book gives this combination of sample size and k for a large enough number of plans to cover the majority of cases for which variables plans are likely to be used in receiving inspection.

6.4. Acceptance Criterion for Double-sampling Plans

The foregoing discussion concerned plans which called for a single sample to be drawn from the lot. Through an extension of the same theory, it has been possible to construct double-sampling plans which permit two samples to be taken from the lot. The first sample of a double-sampling plan is much smaller than the sample for a single-sampling plan having the same risks. As indicated in Sec. 5.2, this first sample will suffice to determine the proper disposition of the lot so long as it has a great many defects or only a few. The acceptance constant k_a for this relatively small first sample has been made large enough so that, if the criterion $\bar{x}_1 + k_a s_1 \leq U$ is met, the lot can safely be accepted. The rejection constant k_r has been made low enough so that there will be sufficient evidence for rejection if the criterion $\bar{x}_1 + k_r s_1 \geq U$ is met.

If the evidence from the first sample indicates that the lot is neither good enough to be accepted nor poor enough to be rejected by these criteria, another sample is drawn to give enough evidence for a final decision. On the basis of the first and second samples combined, a constant k_t is used in the criteria $\bar{x}_t + k_t s_t \leq U$ for acceptance and $\bar{x}_t + k_t s_t > U$ for rejection (or $\bar{x}_t - k_t s_t \geq L$ and $\bar{x}_t - k_t s_t < L$ for a lower limit).

For each of the single-sampling plans a corresponding double-sampling plan has been included which enables lots of different quality to be distinguished from one another in exactly the same manner as the related single-sampling plan. In double sampling, the number of items in the first and second samples combined is somewhat larger than the number in the sample for a corresponding single-sampling plan. However, a decision is very often reached on data from the first sample only. Consequently, for double sampling, the average number of items inspected per lot is considerably less, in the long run, than the number of items inspected per lot under the corresponding single-sampling plan. A choice between the two types is primarily a matter of inspection costs.

More complete information on the determination of the constants and other features of these variables plans is given in Chaps. 10 and 11. Chapter 7 describes the procedure to be used for item characteristics where the specification gives both an upper and lower limit.

7. THE ASSUMPTION OF A NORMAL DISTRIBUTION

In the discussion of the limitations of sampling plans based upon variables inspection, the statement was made that values for the property being inspected must be distributed normally, or almost normally, within the lot. That is, if all the items in the lot were to be measured, the measurements would be distributed among the possible values in a manner similar to the distribution indicated by curve (a) of Fig. 2.3. The most obvious features of this distribution are symmetrical distribution of readings on each side of the average and clustering of readings about the average (represented by the dashed line).

The pattern of the frequency rate as values deviate from the average should be noted in particular. For values near the average the rate of decrease is slight. Then for a considerable range of values the rate of decrease is sharp, until the frequencies become relatively small when it slackens and approaches zero. This pattern of decreasing frequencies gives the so-called bell shape to the normal distribution. The formula for this curve, as well as many other properties of the distribution, can be obtained from any textbook on elementary statistics.

To obtain quality protection close to that promised by the variables plans, the distribution of values within the inspection lot must approximate the normal distribution. All calculations used in constructing the plans have been based upon this assumption. This point is made solely for precautionary reasons and should not alarm the prospective user of the plans. The properties of most raw materials used by industry and of most manufactured products seem to be distributed in forms that are close enough to the normal distribution for the practical use of these variables plans. The main concern of those who use the variables plans should be to acquire the ability to recognize the occasional exceptional cases, so that appropriate allowances can be made or other methods of acceptance inspection used. Practical tests for verifying an assumption of normality are given in Sec. 7.4 of this chapter. If there seems to be a possibility that the product has been screened or if for some other reason

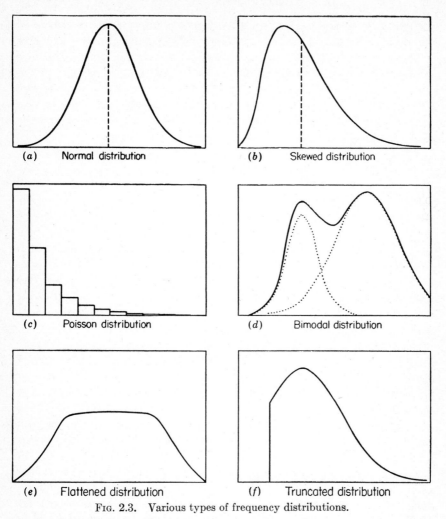

Fig. 2.3. Various types of frequency distributions.

a normal distribution is not approximated, an alternative to variables acceptance sampling is the combined use of variables and attribute plans.

7.1. Skewed Distributions

The most common exception to normality is the skewed distribution. In fact, it seems reasonable to assume that a small amount of skewness is always present. The frequencies in a skewed distribution are not distributed symmetrically about the mean but take the form shown by (b) of Fig. 2.3. The most frequent value, the mode, lies to one side of the mean. Excessive skewness may occur when a variation-producing cause inherent in the material, machine, or operator has a fairly definite limit on only one side of its customary operating range and when the product is manufactured while operating close to this limit. For example, variation in the size of a part depends both upon the variation in hardness of the raw material and upon the pressure of the tool against the material. If the machine elements applying pressure to the tool are working close to a limit of compressibility, a large increase beyond the average hardness in a particular piece of the raw material might cause a relatively slight deviation in size, whereas a comparative decrease in hardness might result in a relatively large deviation in the opposite direction. To give another example, extreme skewness might be found in the distribution of durability among items in a lot. For many products the life expectancy depends upon the consumption of some substance. If consumption were the sole factor limiting the life span, it might not change the normal distribution. But additional limiting factors may exist, and a skewed distribution may result.

When item quality is measured in terms of defects per unit under circumstances where an almost infinite number of such defects are possible, a Poisson distribution is obtained. Here again the distribution is skewed, because values tend to fall near some definite limit, in this case, 0 defects [see (c) of Fig. 2.3]. The smaller the average number of defects per unit, the more skewed the distribution. For this reason, in the preliminary discussion in Chap. 1 the use of variables plans was excluded for item quality measured in terms of defects per unit. The Poisson distribution, however, approaches the normal when the average number of defects per unit increases. Thus, with proper supervision, limited use of the plans may be possible for products with this form of distribution.

7.2. Multimodal and Other Non-normal Distributions

Another form of non-normal distribution that occurs occasionally is the multimodal, a distribution characterized by two or more distinct humps or peaks. Curve (d) of Fig. 2.3 illustrates a typical case, the dotted lines indicating the separate distributions from which this bimodal type arises. When two machines produce the items of an inspection lot with measurements centering around well-separated averages, or when a single machine turns out part of a lot at a low average of measured values and the rest at a higher, a multimodal distribution is the result.

Lack of control during the production of the lot, such that the average of measured values is constantly shifted in one direction, creates yet another form of non-normal distribution. This flattened distribution [curve (e) of Fig. 2.3] may result from an infinite number of hypothetical normal distributions similar to the two in (d) of Fig. 2.3. Tool and die wear may cause this deviation from the normal distribution, although their effects are usually so negligible they are obscured by more powerful causes of variation. If tool wear were considerable, however, during the production of a lot, and if other causes of variation had relatively no effect, then a rectangular form, the limiting case of the flattened distribution, might conceivably appear. One should note that these departures from normality are caused by a lack of control during the production of the lot and not by any lack of control that produces variations in quality from lot to lot. Lack of control that produces variations in quality from lot to lot makes sampling inspection necessary and useful.

A distinct contrast to the flattened distribution is one that rises to an exceptional height at its modal value. But the occurrence of this peaked form in industrial products seems to be uncommon. It is possible that a normal distribution improperly plotted may appear quite peaked or, for that matter, quite flat. Its general ratio of height to width will depend both upon its standard deviation and upon the scales chosen for the graph.

One other exceptional form of distribution that should be carefully watched for arises occasionally in products that have been screened manually before shipment or automatically in the production line. Its graph may be shaped like that in (f) of Fig. 2.3. Should screened lots be submitted to a variables sampling plan, some lots would probably be rejected, a possibility that might lead to considerable embarrassment for the receiver. In general, screened lots should be inspected by an attribute plan. In cases where there is some uncertainty as to whether or not the product has been screened, a procedure using both a variables plan and an attribute plan will prevent the possible rejection of lots that have been screened and at the same time require less inspection than the use of an attribute plan alone.

7.3. Effect of Grouping

The normal distribution of item quality within the lot is represented by a smooth continuous curve. Measured values of any quality characteristic are necessarily grouped into a series of discrete classes. The number of classes depends upon the natural range of values and the precision of measurement. If a dimension varies from 2.025 to 2.050 and micrometer measurements are read and recorded to the nearest 0.001 inch, the data will fall into 25 discrete groups. A recorded value of 2.040 would mean that the true measurement is closer to 2.040 than to 2.039 or 2.041 and that its class interval is 2.0395+ to 2.0405−.

If the number of such class intervals in the distribution falls below ten, the effect of discontinuity may seriously impair the usefulness of the variables plans. For only four or five possible values, the plans are unreliable; the given sampling plans will not ensure sufficient protection because the assumption of normality is seriously violated. Thus, the amount of information per inspected sample item becomes less and less as the number of class intervals decreases, until the variables plan approaches the limiting case of an attribute plan where there are only two classifications of quality. Special plans requiring larger samples would be necessary for equivalent protection in these cases.

If the number of class intervals is increased, there are also certain disadvantages. The accuracy of measurement is limited economically by the higher cost of greater precision in the actual inspection work and by the lower efficiency of recording and calculating because of additional significant figures. In general, a spread of approximately twenty possible values represents a reasonable compromise. Stated in other terms, the largest measured values should differ preferably in the last two significant figures from the smallest measured values.

7.4. Verification of the Assumption of Normality

The acceptance inspection supervisor must see that the variables plans are not used for the quality characteristic which has a non-normal distribution. Experienced knowledge of the materials and processes and awareness of the common causes of unusual patterns of variation are the most effective aids to sound judgment in this regard. In addition, there are several practical tests based upon a simple study of the data in relation to the concept of normal distribution. Inspectors faced with an exceptional situation calling for close examination of the distribution should consult statistical textbooks for more reliable mathematical methods.

(a) Periodic analysis of readings obtained from measurement of sample items. When all possible values (or small class intervals) are listed in order, and when the frequency of recurrence of each value is tallied, inspection of the data in this form should disclose any significant departure from normality. In any event, this analysis should clearly indicate whether the product has a flat or rectangular distribution or whether or not it has been screened. Instead of arranging the data from measurement of sample items in this form, it is also possible to determine from statistical tables what the number of items for each possible measured value would be if the distribution were normal.

(b) Plotting the observed frequencies on ordinary graph paper and drawing a curve through them. This may make a comparison of the actual data with a normal distribution easier.

(*c*) Construction of a histogram, or series of parallel bars, one for each possible value or class interval, making the height of each equal to the frequency for that value.

(*d*) Plotting the observed distribution for a sample on what is known as normal graph paper or probability paper. The scales on this paper are so arranged that a curve of a normal distribution which is properly plotted will be a straight line. The nature of any departure from normality can be known by the way in which the plotted data departs from the straight line. This is a more refined graphical test.

In any of the tests outlined, at least one hundred readings should be used to ensure a reasonable degree of reliability. When the sample size is small, readings from several samples may have to be combined. Care must be taken to group data from lots produced under conditions as similar as possible, for example, on the same day and from the same machine. Otherwise, the distribution of the combined samples may be non-normal because of the difference in lot averages. Even if the test for normality is made on readings from one sample, some non-normality may be indicated in spite of the fact that the distribution of the lot may be normal. Since the sample does not always fairly represent the lot, and since the lot chosen to test for normality does not always fairly represent the process, an accurate picture of the distribution of a product may be difficult to obtain. Fortunately, all that is needed in using the variables sampling plan is some assurance that the product in question is not one of the exceptional cases where the distribution differs radically from the normal.

In one sense, however, the ability of variables plans to control the quality of the accepted product is relatively unaffected by the form of distribution. This should furnish added assurance in the use of variables plans. The relation of the central position and the spread of the distribution of item quality for the lot as a whole to the specification limit can be predicted sufficiently for distributions that are far from normal. There will be a difference between the level of protection in terms of percent defective actually afforded by the use of a plan and the level listed for the plan, the tabled level applying only when used on normal or approximately normal distributions. As outlined in the previous section, the acceptance criteria in a normal distribution are related to the percentage of defective items that lies beyond a specification limit U (see the shaded area in Fig. 2.2). The actual protection received when a variables plan is used for a property which is not normally distributed will differ from the expected protection to the extent that the percentage of items beyond the limit for the distribution in question (which would then be the shaded area under the curve) differs from a normal distribution having the same average and standard deviation. Those in industry who have studied many actual distributions from this standpoint have seldom found significant departures from the normal distribution percentages.

The degree of protection in acceptance inspection cannot be closely determined. Choice of plan must depend upon intangible factors as well as tangible, the effects of which can only be estimated. Costs of accepting a defective item, losses in processing time or in customer's goodwill by letting a defective item leave the plant, the eventual costs of rejecting and returning lots to the supplier—such factors are difficult to assess. It should not be a matter of too much concern, therefore, if the intended degree of protection is not exactly realized.

CHAPTER 3

PROPERTIES OF THE VARIABLES PLANS

1. THE OPERATING CHARACTERISTIC CURVE

As outlined in the preceding chapter, the fraction defective in a sample may be more or less than the actual proportion of defective items in the lot. Under any lot-by-lot inspection plan based on sampling, a lot with too high a percentage of defectives will occasionally be accepted and an acceptable lot will occasionally be rejected. If under a given plan a number of equivalent lots of product are submitted (lots containing the same number of items and the same percentage of defective items in each lot), some lots would be accepted and some rejected, depending upon how chance had affected the drawing of samples. The number of these lots that would be accepted and the number that would be rejected would depend upon both the nature of the inspection plan used and the actual percentage of defective items in the submitted lots. In selecting a sampling plan it is useful to have specific knowledge of how each of the available plans differentiates between good and bad lots. Such information can best be presented as an operating characteristic (OC) curve for each plan.

The OC curve of a typical sampling plan is illustrated in Fig. 3.1. Each point on this curve shows the percentage of submitted inspection lots for their particular percent defective that will be accepted by the plan. For example, if a number of lots containing 0.65 percent defective items were submitted to the plan, 95 percent of them would be accepted according to this OC curve. Another way of expressing this property of the plan is to say that, if a lot containing 0.65 percent defective items were submitted, the probability is 0.95 that it would be accepted. If lots with 3.6 percent of the items defective were submitted, the curve shows that only 10 percent of them would be accepted. For any other percent defective the OC curve will show in a similar manner the chance the lot has of being accepted. Table E gives the OC curves for each of the plans presented in this book.

Just as in the attribute plans, for the OC curves of the variables plans the quality of a lot is expressed in terms of the percentage of items defective. Even though under the variables plans the quality of items is measured along a continuous scale and the quality of the sample as a

25

whole is expressed by the mean and the standard deviation of these measurements, lot quality is nevertheless considered in the familiar terms of the percent defective.   For most products the important requirement is, not that the mean and variability of measurements for the items be at or near some predetermined value, but rather that the measurement of any individual item does not exceed some limit.   In checking the diameter of a part to be used in an assembly, a more vital statistic than the mean diameter or standard deviation is the number of parts exceeding a given diameter, since oversized parts might not enter the assembly or

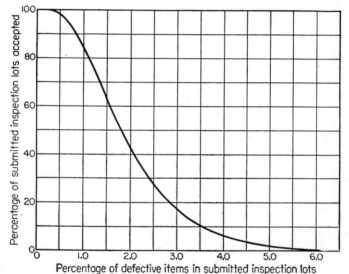

Fig. 3.1.   OC curve of sampling plan whose AQL class is 0.32 to 0.65 percent, sample-size letter J.

might not function properly if assembled.   Therefore, it seems more practical to design the variables plans so that each lot can be judged by its percent defective.

2. CLASSIFICATION OF SAMPLING PLANS; AQL AND LTPD

An infinite variety of acceptance inspection plans are possible, each resulting in a different operating characteristic curve.   Two constants, the value of k and the sample size, determine the curve for single-sample variables plans.   For a given sample size, different values of k produce plans which differ in the general level of protection; the larger the value of k, the more stringent the acceptance criterion.   In other words, the percent defective in submitted lots must be lower for the same proportion of defective lots to be accepted.   In terms of the OC curves, larger values of k give curves farther to the left.   This is illustrated in Fig. 3.2.

The form of the curve depends also upon the absolute size of the sample; the larger the sample, the more likely it is to represent accurately the quality of the lot and the more sharply the good lots are distinguished from the bad in the acceptance procedure.   Evidence of this is reflected in the increasing steepness of the OC curves for successively larger sample sizes (see Fig. 3.3).   Figure 3.3 also shows an angular curve (the dashed line) which represents the ideal plan for differentiating between good and bad lots.   But a plan giving this ideal

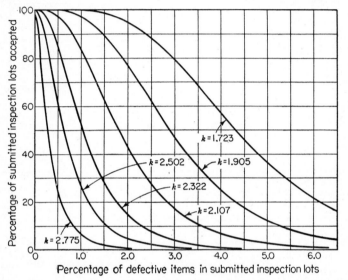

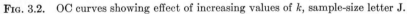

FIG. 3.2.   OC curves showing effect of increasing values of k, sample-size letter J.

curve can be achieved only by inspecting all the items in the lot.   In sampling inspection, how close the OC curve will approach this ideal form depends upon how large a sample can be justified economically.

Table E presents a comprehensive collection of single-sample and double-sample variables plans.   For each corresponding pair of single-sample and double-sample plans an OC curve is given which describes closely the action of both types of plans.

These plans are first classified in terms of sample size.   Sample size is expressed both by a sample-size letter, the reasons for which will be given later, and by number of items.   They are then classified further within each sample size by a value known as the acceptable quality level (AQL). The acceptable quality level is defined as the percentage of defective items in an inspection lot such that the sampling plan will accept 95 percent of all lots submitted containing that percentage of defects. The OC curve of the plan will then pass through the point defined by the AQL. The value of this single point is a convenient way of stating the relative position of the curve.

It would be impractical to compile or use a collection of plans for every possible AQL, and therefore a range of AQL values is covered by each plan. For any value within its AQL range each plan gives probabilities of acceptance close enough for all practical purposes to those indicated by the curves. The actual AQL value of each plan may be read

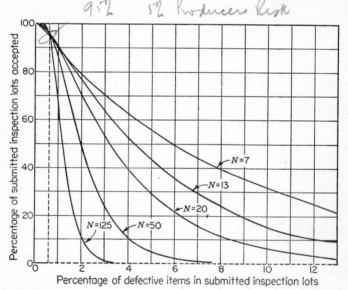

FIG. 3.3.   OC curves showing effect of increasing sample size, AQL class 0.32 to 0.65 percent.

directly from the OC curve or may be obtained from Table D, which shows this value for every AQL class and every sample-size letter.

Sampling plans are often classified by another point on their OC curves, a point called the lot tolerance percent defective (LTPD). The lot tolerance percent defective is the percentage of defective items in an inspection lot such that the sampling plan will reject 90 percent of all lots submitted containing that percentage of defects. This value for each plan may be read from its OC curve or may be found along with the AQL in Table D.

The information afforded each plan either by the OC curve or by the AQL and the LTPD is sufficient to guide management in selecting the most suitable plan in view of the quality that will probably be submitted, the quality desired in the accepted product, and the costs of acceptance inspection.   To strike a proper balance between these factors in choosing a plan, the procedures outlined in Chap. 4 may offer some assistance.

3. DISPOSITION OF REJECTED INSPECTION LOTS AND ITS EFFECT ON THE QUALITY OF THE ACCEPTED PRODUCT; AOQ AND AOQL

3.1. Effect of Variation of Percent Defective from Lot to Lot upon Improvement of Quality

Although the action of a sampling plan for any given lot is not wholly certain, lot-by-lot sampling can raise the over-all quality of the accepted product above the general quality of the product submitted.   A relatively high percentage of the better lots will be accepted under a sampling plan, and a relatively high percentage of the poorer lots rejected. This action, as previously indicated, depends upon a variation in the percent defective from lot to lot.   If the quality of all lots were alike, the acceptance or rejection of a lot would depend entirely upon how chance affected the drawing of the sample, and the average quality of lots finally accepted would of necessity be the same as the quality of the lots as submitted (aside from the negligible improvement if defective items in the sample are discarded).   This assumption of identical submitted lots is obviously unrealistic, however; in almost all manufactured products there is considerable variation in quality from lot to lot. Because there is this difference in percent defective from lot to lot, sampling plans can improve the quality of the accepted product.

3.2. Effect of Disposition of Rejected Inspection Lots upon Improvement of Quality

Improvement of product quality through sampling inspection depends upon another factor, one perhaps not quite so obvious, and that is the proper disposition of rejected inspection lots.   Lots rejected by a sampling plan are usually returned to the supplier.   He will probably do one of two things with these returned lots: (a) dispose of the lots elsewhere by sending them to another customer or by scrapping them; (b) screen the lots, removing, repairing, or replacing all defective items and resubmitting them to the original purchaser as perfect lots.   The supplier also has a third alternative which does not result in any quality improvement: (c) he may resubmit the lots to the original purchaser without doing anything to them.   These three alternatives should be considered from the standpoint of their effect on the quality of the goods finally accepted by the purchaser.

Under alternative (a) in which rejected lots are not resubmitted, the average quality of the accepted product is improved in the manner previously described. The extent of this improvement will depend upon the operating characteristics of the sampling plan and upon the quality of the submitted lots.

Alternative (c), the resubmission of rejected lots to the original receiver without screening or reworking them, is not likely to occur but deserves brief consideration. If such a practice were consistently followed, it is obvious that sampling inspection will have no effect on raising the quality of the accepted product. A poor lot has some chance of acceptance, because there is always the possibility of drawing a sample which is considerably better than the lot. While such chances are small for poor lots, even a lot with an exceptional number of defectives will eventually be passed if resubmitted enough times.

Alternative (b), in which the supplier (or in some cases the receiver) screens the rejected lots and resubmits them to the original receiver after replacing all defective items with good ones, is a common industrial practice. The screened lots that are resubmitted and used along with the other accepted lots raise the average quality of all lots finally accepted above the average quality of the lots originally accepted by the sampling plan. The principal virtue of this procedure is the great improvement in the average quality of all lots finally accepted, even greater than the improvement under alternative (a).

3.3. Average Outgoing Quality (AOQ)

The average quality under alternative (b) is known as average outgoing quality (AOQ). The average outgoing quality can readily be calculated for any submitted quality. For example, suppose that in all submitted lots 1.25 percent of the items are defective, and suppose that the plan the OC curve of which is given in Fig. 3.1 is used. From this curve we observe that about 73 percent of such lots will be accepted. If 100 of these lots are received, 73 would be accepted and 27 rejected. The 73 accepted would be 1.25 percent defective. The 27 returned to the supplier for screening before acceptance would supposedly contain no defectives when finally accepted. The average percent defective in the combined lots (the AOQ) is approximately

$$\frac{73 \times 1.25 + 27 \times 0}{100} = 0.91 \text{ percent}$$

But a number of defectives are removed from the samples of the 73 lots accepted without screening. Neglecting this fact tends to overstate the AOQ. On the other hand, the calculation assumes that the defectives found in the 27 screened lots are replaced with items known to be good, a practice not always followed. This assumption tends to under-

state the AOQ.   It can be easily demonstrated that the combined effect
of these two simplifications does not result in any error of practical
importance.

3.4. Average Outgoing-quality Limit (AOQL)

Under a given sampling plan, if the AOQ's were calculated for each
possible percent defective in the lots originally submitted and if their
values were plotted, the result would be known as an AOQ curve.   The
AOQ curve for the plan used in these illustrations is shown in Fig. 3.4.

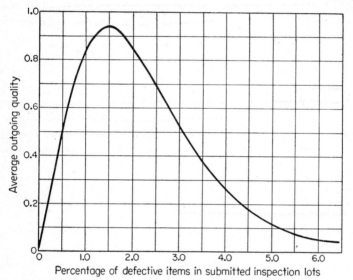

FIG. 3.4.   AOQ curve of sampling plan whose AQL class is 0.32 to 0.65 percent, sample-size letter J.

One should note that this curve has a maximum value or limit.   The
AOQ curve of any sampling plan will have such a limit.   This maximum
value on the AOQ curve is known as the average outgoing-quality limit
of the sampling plan (AOQL).   It may be simply defined as the maximum average percentage of defective items in the product that is finally
accepted if all rejected lots are screened and resubmitted.

The AOQL furnishes another means of describing the action of sampling plans.   Whenever rejected lots are screened and returned, definite
assurance can be obtained about the lowest quality of the accepted product, assurance that the average quality of the product finally accepted,
regardless of the quality of the product originally submitted, can never
be worse than a stated percent defective, the AOQL.   In practice, the
supplier will usually find it profitable to see that the submitted product is

better than the acceptable quality level, and, accordingly, the AOQ will be considerably less than this limit. For those who are interested, an AOQL class is included with each of the plans in this book.

4. SAVINGS IN INSPECTION OF VARIABLES PLANS OVER ATTRIBUTE PLANS

To facilitate general administration of sampling inspection, each plan has been so designed that its operating characteristic curve closely matches the operating characteristic curve of an attribute sampling plan from the set presented in "Sampling Inspection." To facilitate administration further, procedures for the selection and operation of the plans have also been designed on a parallel basis. Consequently, the inspection department is able to choose between a variables and an attribute plan with a considerable degree of independence. The plan chosen will be that which costs the least for the product in question. The expenses to be considered are those incurred in drawing the sample, in actually measuring or gauging the item, in making the required computation, in damaging any item during inspection, in administrating, and possibly in other ways.

Variables sampling inspection usually increases the cost of inspecting an item. More time must be spent in taking and recording the measurements, and more costly equipment often has to be used (except when one relatively inexpensive micrometer can take the place of a number of go–not-go gauges). In addition, an appreciable amount of calculating must be done.

On the other hand, the sample size of a variables plan is smaller. As indicated in the introductory chapter, these particular variables plans have been constructed so that smaller sample sizes can be used in sampling inspection. When the drawing of a sample item from a lot is difficult, when inspection of an item is costly either on an attribute basis or on a variables basis, or when inspection destroys the item, small sample size is an important advantage. Savings resulting from a reduction in sample size may far outweigh any extra costs of inspection or calculations.

To give some indication of the extent of this saving, the reduction in the number of items that have to be inspected is shown for each sample-size letter in Table 3.1. This table compares the sample size under single-sampling variables inspection plans with the sample size under the corresponding single-sampling attribute inspection plans. It shows that percent saving increases as sample size increases. For installations where a large sample is needed, the savings in inspection costs are considerable.

TABLE 3.1.   SAVINGS IN SAMPLE SIZE UNDER VARIABLES PLANS OVER ATTRIBUTE PLANS

Sample-size letter	Sample size under attributes	Sample size under variables	Savings	
			Actual	Percentage
B	10	7	3	30
C	15	10	5	33
D	20	13	7	35
E	30	16	14	47
F	40	20	20	50
G	55	25	30	55
H	75	35	40	53
I	115	50	65	57
J	150	60	90	60
K	225	70	155	69
L	300	85	215	72
M	450	100	350	78
N	750	125	625	83
O	1500	200	1300	87

5. THE CHOICE BETWEEN SINGLE SAMPLING AND DOUBLE SAMPLING

Double-sampling plans are based on the drawing and inspection of a relatively small first sample from each lot and, for some lots, on the subsequent drawing of a second sample.   They serve as an alternative to the single-sample plans.   For double sampling both by variables plans and by attribute plans the average number of items inspected per lot will usually be somewhat less than the number of items inspected per lot under equivalent single-sample plans.   When only one sample is needed in double sampling, a glance at the sample sizes listed for each pair of variables plans reveals a considerable savings in terms of number of items. When a second sample must be taken before a decision can be made on the disposition of a doubtful lot, the two samples combined require more inspection then under the single-sample plan.   The net saving actually realized for a number of lots is determined by the quality level of the submitted product and by the operating characteristic curve common to the pair of plans involved.   In cases where the percent defective in the incoming product is in a range of values slightly higher than the selected AQL, double sampling will often call for more inspection.

When the average number of items inspected per lot is the primary factor determining acceptance inspection costs and when the submitted quality level is somewhat better than the selected AQL, double-sampling plans are usually most economical.   Many suppliers feel that such plans are preferable because they seem to give the lot a "second chance."   But this idea of a second chance is far from being true; all lots have the same probability of acceptance under either type of plan.

Double-sampling plans have certain disadvantages that may offset some of the savings resulting from few sample items per lot. First, the general procedure for evaluating the lot is more involved than that for single sampling and may call for a few more calculations. Double sampling, then, requires more clerical time and may call for closer supervision of personnel. Another disadvantage, and a serious one, arises when the drawing and physical handling of inspection lots requires an appreciable amount of effort and makes it difficult or impossible for the inspector to obtain a second sample. Under such circumstances it may be necessary to draw initially both the first and second samples from every lot, even though it will usually be found that the second one is not needed. A minor disadvantage arises from a secondary use of sampling data. Sampling data is often used in determining the average quality of lots newly submitted and in determining the state of control of the producer's processes. Only data from the first sample in double-sampling plans can properly be used in compiling such information. Since this first sample is relatively small, it yields much less information than the relatively large sample in a corresponding single-sample plan. A final disadvantage of double sampling is the rapid increase, caused by a deterioration of submitted quality, in the average number of items inspected per lot, often to a number well above that for single sampling. In some circumstances this increase may create a peak load of work that will be difficult for the inspection department to absorb.

The double-sampling plans have been designed so that their operating characteristic curves closely match the curves for the single-sample plans of the same AQL class and sample-size letter and, in turn, the curves for the corresponding set of attribute plans. The choice of a plan for a particular product can be made at a supervisory level solely in terms of costs, with the assurance that any type of plan chosen will give equal protection.

6. COMPARISON OF SEQUENTIAL SAMPLING BY ATTRIBUTES WITH SAMPLING BY VARIABLES

In addition to plans using one sample and those using two, plans may be constructed which call for the drawing of more than two samples. These sequential-sampling plans are merely an extension of the procedures for double sampling. Sequential plans reduce even further the average number of items inspected per lot. For reasons given in Chap. 10 it does not seem feasible to design and publish sequential plans for variables. However, plans for sequential sampling by attributes are available in "Sampling Inspection." An inspection program using mainly single sampling by attributes might well consider the alternatives of multiple sampling by attributes and single or double sampling by variables as a means of reducing inspection costs.

Under sequential sampling, a relatively small first sample is taken, the inspection of which may result in the acceptance or rejection of the lot. Often, however, a decision is not reached and a second sample is required. When a second sample is taken and inspected, the data is combined with that of the first sample. If this combined data is not conclusive, a third sample is taken, and so forth. Each sequential plan specifies a definite series of samples and of acceptance and rejection criteria in such a way that, if a decision is not reached before the end of the given number of samples, it is necessarily reached at the end. Under sequential plans, the number of items inspected varies widely from lot to lot, but it is possible to compute how many items will be inspected, on the average, from a lot with a given percent defective. The average sample sizes for the sequential attribute plans are given in "Sampling Inspection" for lot quality at the AQL and for lot quality at the LTPD. The values for the minimum and maximum average sample number (ASN) with lot quality at the AQL and at the LTPD have been tabulated in Table 3.2

TABLE 3.2.   COMPARISON OF SEQUENTIAL SAMPLING BY ATTRIBUTES WITH SAMPLING BY VARIABLES

Sample-size letter	Single-sample size	Sampling by variables				Sequential sampling by attributes			
			Double sampling						
		Min ASN at AQL	Max ASN at AQL	Min ASN at LTPD	Max ASN at LTPD	Min ASN at AQL	Max ASN at AQL	Min ASN at LTPD	Max ASN at LTPD
B	7	5	7	5	6	6	10	6	9
C	10	8	9	8	10	9	13	8	11
D	13	11	11	11	13	14	17	12	14
E	16	13	13	14	15	17	26	15	20
F	20	16	17	19	20	24	35	21	27
G	25	20	20	20	21	29	47	27	34
H	35	27	28	28	32	38	90	38	62
I	50	36	38	38	41	54	131	53	89
J	60	47	47	48	49	73	174	74	119
K	70	51	53	58	63	96	230	98	164
L	85	65	67	67	69	128	306	139	200
M	100	76	76	77	78	223	518	219	335
N	125	92	94	94	102	348	631	307	452
O	200	151	154	156	164	783	1324	722	1121

for each sample-size letter. If a decision is to be made as to whether to use sequential sampling by attributes or single or double sampling by variables, these average sample numbers for the attribute plans may be compared with the single-sample sizes for variables and to the average-sample sizes for double sampling by variables. For sample-size letters B and C, both single and double variables plans have almost the same magnitude as that of the expected number of observations at the AQL for the sequential attribute plans. For sample-size letters D through J, the variables single-sample size is smaller than the corresponding sequential ASN, and the savings are substantial for letters K through O. The savings in the use of double-sampling variables plans over sequential sampling attribute plans are more pronounced; for sample-size letters D through I the saving is considerable, and for the higher sample-size letters the savings amount to as much as 77 percent at the AQL. Similar remarks hold for the ASN's at the LTPD. However, in comparing sample sizes, the other advantages and disadvantages of variables and sequential attribute plans must not be overlooked; the saving achieved through the reduction of the number of items sampled by use of a variables plan may not compensate for the increased cost of individual item measurements and for the greater amount of record keeping and computational work involved.

7. PRESCRIBED SAMPLE SIZES

The extent to which good and bad lots can be distinguished from one another varies directly with the size of the sample. Section 2 indicated that the larger the sample, the better can the distinction be made between good and bad lots. But on the other hand, the larger the sample, the greater the total costs of receiving inspection for the lot. The sample sizes selected for these variables plans constitute a practical balance between inspection costs and quality protection.

In using the plans it might be possible to assemble relatively large inspection lots from which large samples could appropriately be taken. This would result in a relatively low inspection cost per unit of submitted product. But in order for any type of sampling plan to be effective, inspection lots must be formed in such a manner that the greatest possible variation is maintained in quality from lot to lot. The formation of relatively large lots by the indiscriminate grouping of items would tend to level out existing variations and would thus make rejection of relatively low-quality sections of product difficult. Hence, inspection lots must be formed more or less independently of any consideration of sample size. When this practice is observed, lots will be large for some products and small for others. In addition the size of the lot for a particular product may vary from time to time under certain conditions.

It would also be possible, if one wished, to select a sample size independently of the size of the inspection lot and then to draw and inspect this number of items. Under plans where this practice is observed, differentiation of good and bad lots can be made almost as well for large lots as for small ones. This nearly constant degree of protection would be desirable from a standpoint of quality alone. Acceptance inspection costs per unit of product submitted would, however, vary greatly. The costs per unit would be relatively low for products from which large inspection lots could appropriately be formed; the unit costs might be prohibitively high if the inspection lots were necessarily small. On the other hand, one might go to the extreme and take a sample the size of which is a fixed percentage of the inspection lot, a practice commonly followed. Inspection costs per unit submitted would then be held approximately constant. But if this practice were observed, varying degrees of differentiation between good and bad lots would be the undesirable result. A relatively small degree of protection would be provided products from which small inspection lots are formed, and perhaps an unnecessarily large degree of protection would be given a product from which large inspection lots are assembled.

A compromise is necessary, then, in assigning a sample size, a compromise between constant inspection costs per unit submitted and a constant degree of acceptance protection. For the smaller lot sizes, the sample size must be a value that will not lead to excessively high inspection costs per unit submitted; for the larger inspection-lot sizes, the sample size may well be somewhat increased to provide better quality distinction without increasing inspection costs per submitted unit. How directly the sample size should vary with an increase or decrease in the size of the inspection lot is a practical matter and cannot be determined with any exactness. More or less arbitrary values, representing what seems to be a reasonable and workable compromise under normal conditions, have been assigned in the case of the attribute plans. The number of items inspected per lot increases as the size of the lot increases, but the percentage of items inspected decreases. In the variables plans presented in this book the sample sizes selected are those necessary to produce operating characteristics closely matching the operating characteristics for the attribute plans.

Under the procedure established for the selection and use of the variables plans, a sample-size letter is chosen, the choice depending primarily on the size of the inspection lot. Appropriate letters for each of a connected series of lot-size ranges are given in Table A. Inasmuch as the two basic types of variables plans and the three types of attribute plans are available on a parallel basis, each calling for different numbers of items in its sample or samples, use of the sample-size letter instead of actual sample sizes is almost essential in their classification, selection, and use.

8. THE INSPECTION LEVEL

In the determination of sample size some latitude has been provided the user for striking a balance between a high degree of protection and low inspection costs for acceptance. Before determining an appropriate sample-size letter from Table A, one chooses an inspection level. Under ordinary conditions of acceptance inspection, the expectation is that operation will be by normal inspection, which is usually achieved by having a sample-size letter chosen from the column in Table A headed inspection level II. Sample sizes determined by choosing letters from this column represent what seems to be a practical compromise for most situations. But when the conditions of acceptance inspection are not normal, when, for example, the acceptance of a defective item is a serious matter and the cost of inspecting an item is relatively low, inspection level III might be used for normal inspection. Here larger sample sizes are specified in order to reduce acceptance risks. If, on the other hand, acceptance of a defective item is not so serious, inspection level I, which specifies smaller sample sizes, might be considered most appropriate for normal inspection.

9. REDUCED AND TIGHTENED INSPECTION

An optional technique is available for changing the amount of inspection when significant changes in the quality of a product submitted are noted. Under normal inspection the receiver may find, for example, that the quality of a submitted product has been running consistently and considerably better than the quality he would be willing to tolerate. He may find it appropriate to cut inspection costs by reducing the size of the sample. Although there is a greater risk of accepting a low-quality lot, use of a smaller sample is in order when there is evidence that only a few lots of poor quality are being submitted. Under the procedure established for the plans, the proper reduction in sample size is accomplished by going on reduced inspection. To go on reduced inspection means that the sample-size letter will be taken from the inspection level just lower (if there is one) than the level in use for normal inspection. For example, if inspection level II has been used for normal inspection, inspection level I is used for reduced inspection. This shift will give a sample-size letter from one to three letters lower and will reduce inspection costs accordingly.

On the other hand, if a supplier's quality level should be found considerably worse than the desired AQL, tightened inspection will be necessary when normal inspection does not give sufficient protection against the acceptance of low-quality lots as will commonly be the case. Tightened inspection is achieved by choosing a value for k from a lower AQL class than the one that would normally be used for the product. This gives a correspondingly higher value for k and so stiffens the requirements for acceptance. The inspection level is not increased. Inspection could be tightened by having a higher inspection level chosen with the attendant increase in sample size, but the receiver would be penalized by higher inspection costs. When tightened or reduced inspection is utilized, return to normal inspection is made as soon as the supplier's incoming product warrants it. For those who may wish to add the above features to the basic procedures, further details will be given in Chap. 5, Sec. 7.

CHAPTER 4

INSTALLATION OF THE VARIABLES PLANS

1. DETERMINATION OF WHAT AN ITEM OF PRODUCT SHOULD BE

The first step in the selection and installation of a sampling inspection plan is the determination of what an item of product should be. In most cases this decision can be made easily; an item will be an individual part, such as a bolt or a gear, or it will be a completed assembly, such as an electric motor, a fuse, or a screwdriver. Sometimes individually purchased parts or assemblies are used in pairs or small groups, and it would be more suitable to consider the pair or the group as the item. In inspecting gloves, for example, a pair might be the appropriate unit. When the product is not received in clearly discrete units of any sort, as is the case for oil, copper tubing, paint, and like materials, the decision is difficult and will often have to be made arbitrarily.

Any decision as to what should constitute an item of product for inspection purposes depends primarily upon the ultimate use of the item. If insulated copper wire were purchased in spools to be made into appliance cords 6 feet long, a 6-foot length of such wire would be the most suitable inspection item. A general knowledge of how the product is produced—whether unit by unit, in batches, or on a continuous basis— and of how it is grouped or divided for packaging should also furnish some guidance. Often, too, the design or purchase specifications will lead to a partial or complete answer to the problem.

2. LISTING OF DEFECTS FOR WHICH THE ITEM IS TO BE INSPECTED

After the item of product has been determined, the next preliminary step to the installation of a variables sampling plan is the clear establishment of what makes the item defective. More than likely, this step has been taken already in the preparation of the purchase specification. If not, it is necessary to list the characteristics for which the item is to be measured and to specify the limits for such measurements beyond which the item will be considered defective. Methods for making these inspections must also be outlined if they have not been done so previously.

When one is determining the characteristics for which the item is to be measured, it is important to know the consequences of accepting each possible type of defect. Some defects in accepted parts or materials are serious, because they prevent the final product from functioning properly or cause expensive production delays in subsequent processing. Other defects may be of such a nature that they can be detected and the item rejected with relatively no loss in subsequent processing and assembly. Still others may permit the product of which the defective item is a part to function, although not so well as one with an item meeting the specifications. A knowledge of the seriousness of each possible type of defect will be needed to select appropriate sampling plans.

According to the attribute inspection procedure in "Sampling Inspection" and according to other existing attribute plans, when the item is inspected at the receiving station for a number of defects, the defectives found in a sample are classified under "major defects" or "minor defects" and the acceptance criterion is applied to the totals under these two groupings. A similar grouping of defects cannot be made for the variables plans, because the acceptance criterion is applied to measurements from sample items, and procedures for combining measurements on several quality characteristics are not available. Thus for the variables plans the acceptance criterion must be applied individually to each type of defect.

3. SELECTION OF AN ACCEPTABLE QUALITY LEVEL (AQL) FOR EACH DEFECT

Next it must be decided, presumably at intermediate or upper levels of inspection management, what quality level in terms of the percentage of defective items can be accepted.   A plan is selected on the basis of an acceptable quality level. As previously defined, the acceptable quality level (AQL) is the percentage of defective items in an inspection lot such that 95 percent of all lots submitted containing that percentage of defects are accepted by the sampling plan.   In actual practice an AQL range is chosen. Fifteen ranges covering all percent defectives from 0.024 to 11.0 are available. That sampling plan which includes the desired AQL within its range is used.   If several characteristics of varying importance are measured, a separate AQL range must be selected for each.

The selection of an AQL range depends almost invariably upon a compromise between the quality that is likely to be submitted by the supplier and the quality that is ideal from a use standpoint (0 percent defective). The engineering and production staffs of the receiver can estimate the percent defective that can be tolerated from an economic or technical point of view. The quality level one can reasonably expect from the supplier can best be determined from experience. In lieu of any experience with the item for which the plan is selected or with like items, some information might possibly be obtained from the supplier.

An estimate of the quality currently obtainable should be made as close as possible in terms of percent defective, and if this estimate represents a satisfactory working quality, the AQL should be selected at or near this value. If the estimate of incoming quality is better (a lower percent defective) than the quality one is willing to tolerate, and particularly if this estimate represents the best figure from a number of possible suppliers, it would be wise to make the AQL somewhat higher than this estimate, so that the acceptance criterion will be less exacting, fewer lots will be rejected, and costs will be reduced for all concerned. On the other hand, should the estimate for incoming quality be a higher percentage than the percent defective one can reasonably accept and use, the AQL class should be set at a lower percentage than the estimate, provided that the rejection of an excessive number of lots will not hamper the receiver's operations. A large number of rejections will ordinarily force the supplier to improve the quality of his lots.

An evaluation of some or all of the following factors should be used in determining how far the AQL for a given product can depart from the estimate of incoming quality.

(*a*) The expense of other forms of loss incurred by the acceptance of a defective item. Where a defective item is not immediately apparent, considerable processing and assembly time may be spent and other materials wasted before it is discovered. In some cases a defective cannot be detected in any way until after it has formed part of an assembly and has caused the final product to function improperly in the hands of the consumer. Whenever considerable tangible or intangible loss results from the acceptance of defectives, the AQL should be lowered to give more acceptance protection. If an item is inspected for more than one defect, a different AQL must be selected for each defect, the value for each depending upon its seriousness.

(*b*) The urgency of demand for the product and the quality level of the source of supply. Sometimes a source of supply cannot be found with a quality level close to the level normally tolerated, and the items involved may be greatly needed. The AQL used in selecting the sampling plan will then have to be set somewhat higher than the level tolerated in order to avoid excessive rejections. If this practice is necessary, efforts should be made to have lots of better quality submitted in the future, so that the AQL can eventually be lowered to a satisfactory level.

(*c*) The possibility of improvement in quality by the supplier. Whenever one's experience or information obtained from other sources leads one to believe that the supplier could easily improve the quality of his product, a somewhat lower AQL should be used in order to furnish an incentive for such a change by the rejection of a large number of inspection lots. This practice could be followed even when the expected quality of lots submitted is better than the level that would be tolerated. The receiver should realize, however, that eventually he may have to pay the costs of achieving quality improvement by this form of pressure, and therefore considerable care should be exercised in applying such pressure to the supplier.

(*d*) The relation of standard quality specifications to actual needs. When specific information about quality needs is lacking, quality specifications are often made quite stringent to ensure a sufficient margin for error. If specification limits appear to be set unduly tight, the AQL selected can be a higher percentage than one might otherwise choose. If the limits appear to correspond closely to actual needs or to be somewhat loose, the AQL selected can be a lower percentage.

(*e*) Changes in condition. An AQL can be changed at any time in accordance with changes in the factors outlined above.

Instead of selecting a sampling plan in terms of an AQL, selection can be made in terms of an AOQL, since the variables plans are so identified and catalogued. Some discussion of this possibility is presented in Sec. 10 of the next chapter. For those who prefer to consider protection from a sampling plan in other terms than that of the AQL or the AOQL, the operating characteristic curves should furnish sufficient information for a proper choice of plans.

4. SELECTION OF AN INSPECTION LEVEL

The next in the series of steps preliminary to the installation of a plan is the selection of an inspection level. As previously indicated, in drawing sample items there is always some risk that the resulting sample will not accurately represent the lot, the extent of the risk varying largely with the absolute size of the sample. The magnitude of this risk can be controlled in the variables plans by selecting an inspection level from one of three provided.

The selected inspection level, as well as the lot size, determines the actual number of items that will constitute a sample. The sample size thus determined represents a compromise between large samples which serve as a more accurate indication of the quality of the lots from which they are drawn and small samples which reduce acceptance inspection costs. The range of sizes which is most reasonable in view of the conditions generally prevailing in industrial practice is covered by the three inspection levels. Inspection level I calls for samples of relatively small size, thereby limiting the extent to which high-quality lots can be distinguished from the low but at the same time minimizing acceptance inspection costs. Somewhat larger samples are specified by inspection level II, and the extent to which distinction of quality can be made is increased at the price of higher inspection costs. Inspection level III calls for sample sizes that are even larger. These samples yield measurements which represent most accurately the quality of the lots from which they are drawn, and inspection level III thus affords the highest degree of protection.

The three inspection levels are provided for each range of lot sizes. For any given inspection-lot size, the amount of inspection in terms of the relative number of items called for under each level is approximately as follows:

Inspection Level	Relative Amount of Inspection
I	1
II	$1\frac{1}{2}$
III	2

There is some variation in these figures for extremely large or extremely small lot sizes.

For the majority of products under the ordinary conditions of acceptance inspection, inspection level II represents a reasonable compromise between the high inspection costs of large samples and the acceptance risks of small sample sizes and should be the level normally used. Certain circumstances, however, may necessitate the use of another level. Among the factors that should be considered in making a choice are:

(a) Possibility of using lots with a quality level lower than the AQL. If there is some reluctance to accept defective lots, level II should be used, and if there is considerable reluctance, level III should be used. Level I with its reduced inspection costs can be used only when there is relatively no reluctance to accept lots with a comparatively high percentage of defectives.

(b) Availability of inspection personnel and facilities. If the number of qualified inspectors and the amount of space and equipment are small in relation to the volume of submitted product, the amount of inspection per lot may of necessity be reduced. This reduction can be effected by choosing a lower inspection level than that normally used, but such emergency measures should not be continued any longer than necessary.

(c) Possibility of a product going on reduced inspection for an indefinite period. This possibility arises during the operation of a sampling plan when the product submitted by the supplier proves to be considerably better than the selected AQL. The procedure for determining when and how to use reduced inspection is discussed in Sec. 7 of the next chapter.

A glance at the operating characteristic curves accompanying the plans listed in Table E shows how much sample size affects the extent to which good lots can be distinguished from poor by the plans. Perhaps an even more convenient way of making this comparison is to refer to Table D, in which the AQL and the LTPD are listed side by side for each of the plans. The difference between the AQL and the LTPD is an excellent indication of the slope of the OC curve or the extent to which differentiation of quality can be made by the plan.

5. DETERMINATION OF THE SIZE OF THE INSPECTION LOT

An inspection lot has been defined as a group of items separated to undergo the acceptance procedure and accepted or rejected as a whole by the inspection of a random sample containing relatively few items. The size or composition of an inspection lot does not necessarily bear any direct relationship to an order lot, a shipping lot, a truck or freight-car load, or perhaps to the number in a shipping container. These lots or loads are broken up or combined, as the case may be, in order to form suitable lots for acceptance inspection.

In the discussion of basic principles in Chap. 1 the point was made that in order for a sampling-inspection plan to be effective there must be variation in quality from lot to lot. The more pronounced this variation, the greater the improvement that can be made in the quality of the accepted product. A simple way of ensuring maximum variation is to combine as infrequently as possible product from different machines, different lines, different plants, or different dates. In other words, inspection lots should be formed of items produced under conditions which are substantially the same in so far as it is possible for the receiver to determine. If the product from different machines, for example, is mixed prior to or during combination into inspection lots, any difference between the quality of output of the machines will be lost, and if the mixing has been thorough, the quality will be substantially the same from one inspection lot to the next. The acceptance or rejection of a given lot would then depend upon the effect of chance in the drawing of the sample; when the quality of the sample picked at random is poor, the lot is rejected, and when the quality is good, the lot is accepted. Mixing product prevents improvement of quality by sampling inspection.

The following suggestions may be of assistance in forming inspection lots. They are not intended to be used as hard-and-fast rules for all cases. One's own judgment concerning the producer's processes must be exercised, and many specific details, such as the way the item is packed and grouped for shipment or the extent to which the item can be identified with production dates, particular machines, and other pertinent production factors, must be considered.

(a) Do not combine product from different molds, dies, patterns, or other formed tools.

(b) Do not combine product from different plants, production lines, or machines or from different production methods.

(c) Do not combine product made by different operators. Varying degrees of skill and effort can affect product quality considerably.

(d) Do not combine product from different shifts.

(e) Do not combine product made from different batches of raw material or from different batches of parts.

Implicit adherence to the above suggestions, however, could lead to two undesirable results. In the first place, the product might be subdivided into such small inspection lots that the inspection costs for the receiver would be excessively large. Second, separating and identifying the product in accordance with all the above suggestions might be too expensive for the supplier. Only the most important factor or factors that lead to quality variation, therefore, are usually taken into consideration in packing and identifying submitted material and in forming inspection lots.

Subject to the important requirement of variability, the inspection lot should be made as large as possible. The larger the lot, the larger the sample size that can be used economically. The larger the sample size, the greater the possibility of distinguishing differences of quality by the sampling plan. Since acceptance inspection costs are primarily determined by the percentage of items inspected, larger inspection lots permit the use of larger samples and consequently either better protection without increasing the inspection cost per unit submitted or the same protection at a lower inspection cost. One should realize clearly, however, that the advantages of large inspection lots are partially or entirely lost if their formation requires the grouping of product that differs considerably in quality. The lot size should reflect a compromise between the reduced inspection costs of large lots and the increased quality improvement of the small lots produced under the same manufacturing conditions.

When one has had no experience with the product or cannot weigh all the essential factors accurately, perhaps the best general rule is to make the lot size large enough to keep inspection costs at a reasonable level, giving as much consideration as possible to the most important factor or factors that lead to variation in product quality.

6. DETERMINATION OF THE SAMPLE-SIZE LETTER

A letter of the alphabet is arbitrarily assigned to represent a certain numerical sample size or, in the case of double sampling, a certain pair of sample sizes. For the plans in this book, the letters run through O. The letter B represents a sample size of 7 for single sampling and a first sample size of 4 and a second sample size of 8 for double sampling; the letter O represents a sample of size of 200 for single sampling and a first sample of 85 and a second sample of 170 for double sampling. The sample sizes associated with each letter are given in Table E.

The determination of the sample-size letter, the next step in the procedure for installing a plan suitable for a given application, depends entirely upon the size of the inspection lot and upon the inspection level that has been selected. Table A lists the sample-size letters for all possible combinations of these two determining factors.

The sample-size letters do not represent the same sample size for both the variables and the attribute plans, since the samples for the variables plans are always smaller. But the sample-size letters are so designed and classified that the variables sample size for both single and double sampling furnishes the same amount of protection as the attribute single-, the attribute double-, and the attribute sequential-sample size. For example, if sample-size letter H is used, the single-sampling variables plans which use a sample of 35 items will have virtually the same operating characteristic curve as the single-sample attribute plans which use a sample of 75 items. The selection of a sample-size letter and an AQL class determines the degree of protection for a plan regardless of the type of plan selected or of the number of items in the sample.

7. THE CHOICE BETWEEN SINGLE AND DOUBLE SAMPLING

In Sec. 5 of Chap. 3 two forms of sampling by variables inspection, single and double, are discussed and the uses of each outlined. As part of the installation procedure a choice must now be made between these two available forms. Although single sampling has been the form generally used, double sampling should be considered, and a choice made only after an evaluation of the following points:

(*a*) The total cost of inspecting an item. The total cost should include the expenses incurred in drawing the item from the lot, in inspecting it, and in damaging any item during inspection. The higher this total, the more likely the variables plans will be used instead of the attribute and, in particular, the double-sample variables plans instead of the single-sample.

(*b*) The experience of inspectors in making computations. As compared with the computations for single-sampling plans those for double sampling are more complicated. Awareness of this particular major disadvantage of double sampling is especially important when sampling inspection by variables is first introduced into an organization. But after familiarizing themselves with the variables procedures and the calculations involved, most inspectors should have relatively no difficulty in using the double-sampling technique.

(c) The possibilities of drawing a second sample from the lot. In double sampling, it is usually more economical to draw the second sample from the lot only after the first sample has been drawn and inspected and the drawing of a second sample found necessary. But this practice is not always easy to follow. If in addition the costs of drawing initially both samples from the lot are high, single sampling might be preferable.

(d) The ability of the inspection staff to care for peak loads. The average sample size in double sampling varies widely because it varies with the quality of incoming product. For many of the plans, when submitted quality becomes somewhat worse than the AQL, a second sample is required so often that the average number of items inspected per lot will be greater than the number for single sampling. But there is the possibility that only occasionally will an appreciable peak load develop for a product from this cause. Furthermore, when many products are inspected, such peaks may be insignificant in comparison with total inspection activity.

(e) The amount of information about quality needed for other purposes. If sampling inspection data is essential to the supplier for control purposes, or if an accurate estimate of the average quality of the submitted product must be obtained without delay, single sampling should be used. In double sampling, only data from the small first sample can properly be used for these purposes.

(f) The "second chance" supposedly given by double sampling. Although the concept of a second chance is fallacious, the supplier may think that a second sample gives a doubtful inspection lot another chance for acceptance and on this basis may advocate the use of double sampling.

As an alternative to single sampling by variables, sequential sampling by attributes can be considered for some products. The inspection and the calculations involved may be easier. On the other hand, the average number of items inspected per lot may be considerably more, particularly for sample-size letters K through O. The drawing of several samples from the lot often introduces additional problems and costs. For a more complete discussion of this alternative see Sec. 6, Chap. 3.

8. DETERMINATION OF THE SPECIFIC PLAN TO APPLY

After the preceding steps have been taken and a sample-size letter selected, it is now possible to determine the specific plan or plans that can be used for the product. This is the last step preparatory to actual acceptance inspection. The plans for both single sampling and double sampling are presented in Table E. From this table the appropriate plan is found first by locating the group of plans listed for the selected sample-size letter and second by selecting the plan from this group which includes

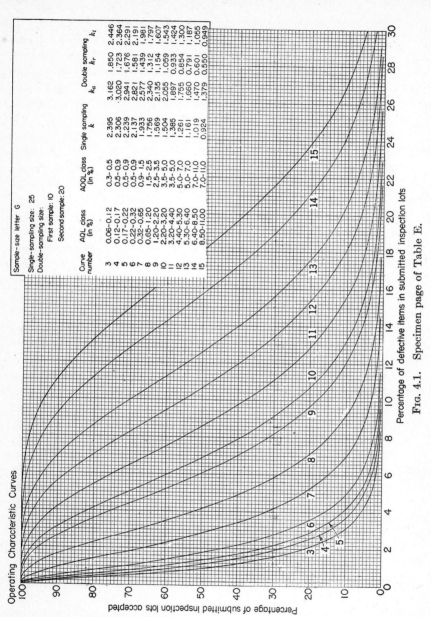

FIG. 4.1. Specimen page of Table E.

the desired AQL within its AQL class. When a product is inspected for several defects with different AQL's, a plan must be selected for each.

A page of representative plans taken from Table E is shown in Fig. 4.1. The area blocked out in the upper right-hand corner includes the necessary data for the selection and operation of these sampling plans. The sample-size letter is listed first. Under this will be found the sample size for single sampling and the first and second sample sizes for double sampling. These sample sizes apply to all the plans on the page.

Under the sample size data the following information is given:

(a) Curve numbers referring to the OC curves shown on the sheet and corresponding to the range of AQL classes covered by the sample-size letter. From these curves, the probability of acceptance of lots containing any given percentage of defective items (within the range of the curves) can be read, and one can thus see how sharply the good lots are distinguished from the poor by each plan. Each AQL class is numbered, and this numbering is used consistently throughout Table E; thus, number 1 refers to AQL class 0.024 to 0.035, number 2 to AQL class 0.035 to 0.06, and so on. Therefore the same-numbered curves appearing on sheets for different sample-size letters represent plans giving the same degree of protection at the AQL. If it is desired to change from one sample-size letter to another but to continue sampling under the same AQL class, this is accomplished by using that sheet of Table E which corresponds to the new sample-size letter and the same-numbered OC curve as used previously.

(b) The AQL classes for the plans on the page. The AQL class for a plan is the range of AQL's it is intended to cover. The actual AQL for the plan can be read from its OC curve or can be found directly in Table D.

(c) The average outgoing quality limit class (AOQL) for those who wish to select plans in these terms.

(d) The values for k, the constant used in the basic acceptance criterion for single sampling.

(e) The values for k_a, k_r, and k_t, the three constants used in the acceptance criteria for double sampling.

Values of the constant k for all single-sampling plans are summarized in Table B. The lot tolerance percent defective (LTPD) for each plan is given in Table D. Table C presents a summary of the plans for double sampling. The OC curves for the double-sampling plans have not been given, since they match the related single-sampling curves closely.

9. RESPONSIBILITY FOR THE INSTALLATION OF PLANS

In industrial concerns of medium or large size or in branches of the Federal government such as the Navy or the Army, the direction of inspection activities and related work concerned with product quality are usually divided among the several levels of management. The procedures for the selection and use of these variables plans follow the pattern for the attribute plans, a pattern that permits a logical division of responsibilities for the various phases of the system.

At an executive level, one or perhaps several persons must assume the responsibility for determining the quality for purchased goods and material. To perform this executive function it must be decided what the item of product is, what properties of the item must be measured and what limits established for these measurements, what AQL should be selected for each possible defect, and which inspection level should be chosen. These are the first four steps in the standard procedure for selecting a sampling plan as outlined in Secs. 1 to 4 of this chapter. The performance of these four steps establishes the quality requirements for the product.

The next responsibility, selection of the plan or plans that will best secure this desired quality under the prevailing conditions, can best be carried out in a large organization at a lower level of inspection supervision, usually by the supervisor in charge of acceptance inspection. This person decides the composition of the inspection lot, determines the sample-size letter, chooses the plan which is most economical in operation, and selects the plan for each inspected characteristic. These decisions made in the steps outlined in Secs. 5 to 8 depend upon the more detailed information available at this lower level about the conditions under which acceptance inspection is going to be performed.

CHAPTER 5

OPERATION OF THE VARIABLES PLANS

1. FORMATION OF INSPECTION LOTS

After a specific plan has been selected for the acceptance inspection of a product, the first step in operating under the plan is to group the incoming product into inspection lots. The number of items that shall make up such lots and the basis on which items are to be selected for inclusion in a given lot have already been determined as outlined in Sec. 5 of Chap. 4.

This step is usually an easy one to carry out. However, a few points must be kept in mind. First, the items that make up a lot should be physically segregated or very clearly marked, so that there will be no confusion among lots. Second, when there are many lots, a system of lot numbers or some other plan for lot identification should be devised. Appropriate identification marks should then be attached to the lots in such a way that they will remain with the lots until the lots are put into stock or disposed of in some other way. And third, if possible the product should be stacked or otherwise placed when assembling the inspection lot, so that each item will be readily available to the inspector when drawing the sample.

If, for economic reasons, groups of items that can be clearly identified as having been made on different days, on different machines, or by different operators have been grouped into one lot, such sublots should be kept separate to assist in proper drawing of the sample. As will be described in the next section, proportional samples will be drawn in such a case. However, the inspection lot will be accepted or rejected in its entirety.

2. DRAWING OF SAMPLES

Most inspection plans based on sampling assume that sample items are drawn at random from the lot. These variables plans are no exception to this general rule; the sample should be drawn by a process that comes as close as possible to being effectively random. Strictly speaking, an item is drawn at random only if, in the drawing, every item that remains in the lot has an equal chance of being drawn—regardless of its quality, of its location in the lot, of what other items have been selected, or of any other circumstance. Selecting an item truly at random is difficult.   Possible practices of the inspector, such as taking most of the items from near the top of cartons, can easily lead to non-random samples which will be misleading in deciding the disposal of the lots.   Some assurance of drawing satisfactory samples may be obtained, however, if the inspector observes the following rules:

(a) Draw items without regard for their apparent quality; neither search for nor attempt to avoid defective or apparently defective items. If defective items are obvious at first glance, this may be a difficult rule to follow.   In such cases, one solution sometimes employed is for the inspector to decide in advance, or for his superior to decide for him, the specific location from which items will be selected.   Fortunately, this problem will very seldom arise for items submitted to variables inspection.

(b) Draw items without regard for their location in the lot.   Or, to restate this rule, draw items from all sections of the lot.   If items are taken from only the tops or from only the center sections of containers, if items are never taken from near or at the bottom of the container, or if like practices are followed, misleading samples may very likely be obtained.   For some products and some packaging methods, adherence to this rule may be difficult, but it should be observed as well as possible. If, in assembling and arranging the inspection lots, some care is taken to make all items readily accessible, this will assist considerably.

(c) Draw proportional samples.   Sometimes, in order to form lots large enough to keep acceptance inspection costs within reasonable limits, an inspection lot is made up of items produced under several conditions known to be different.   For instance, items produced by different production lines on different days or from different lots of raw material might be combined.   In this case, the inspection lot should be divided into sublots, according to the factors that may lead to variations in quality.   Then, when drawing the sample, some items should be taken from each sublot, the number of items from each sublot being proportional to the size of the sublot and of a magnitude to yield the right total sample size.   For example, suppose a lot is composed of 1,000 items, 700 of which were produced on Machine A and 300 on Machine B, and that a sample of 50 items is to be drawn.   Of these 50, 35 items would be drawn from the sublot produced by Machine A and 15 items from the sublot produced by Machine B.   This rule calling for the drawing of a proportional sample may seem to violate the concept of randomness in that, when drawing each item, every other item in the inspection lot does not have the same chance of being drawn.   However, this method does give a closer approach to random sampling than other sampling methods available in this situation.

3. INSPECTION OF ITEMS IN THE SAMPLE

The next step in the operation procedure is to take and record the measurements of the quality characteristic or characteristics for each item in the sample. This is the final step prior to the calculations that will be made to decide whether or not to accept the lot. If two or more characteristics of an item are to be measured, the completion of all such measurements before making any computations is usually desirable. It is true that, if the information gained from measurements of one quality element results in the rejection of the lot, the measurements of the other properties are unnecessary for an acceptance criterion. However, data on the other characteristics is needed for the computation of the process average and should also be available for possible use by the supplier. When a double-sampling plan is used, these remarks apply only to the first sample and do not apply to items in the second sample; if, after drawing a necessary second sample, rejection for one type of defect is indicated, measurements need not be taken on the remaining properties.

4. CALCULATIONS TO DETERMINE DISPOSAL OF THE LOT

Using the data on items in the sample as obtained in the previous step, routine calculations are made to decide under the selected plan (or plans) whether or not to accept the lot. These calculations determine certain general properties of the sample; from these sample properties the lot is evaluated in turns of the criteria established in the acceptance plan. If more than one characteristic of the item is inspected, separate calculations are made for each and the lot is accepted only if every characteristic meets its acceptance standard.

To avoid possible confusion, all details of the computations for the single-sample plans will be discussed first. This will be followed by a separate explanation of computations for double-sampling plans. Both discussions will deal only with properties whose measurements have a single, or one-sided, specification limit, that is, whose measurements must be either over a specified value or under a specified value to be satisfactory and are not required to be between two limiting values. The procedure for measurements with two-sided limits will be covered in Chap. 7.

4.1. Calculations for Single-sample Plans

The following are the calculations, separated into simple steps, that are made for each measured characteristic. Assume that measurements have been made for a sample, the number of items in the sample being represented by n, the measurement of a given characteristic for any one item being represented by x.

(*a*) Calculate the mean $\bar{x}$ of the measurements for the sample. The mean is a simple average obtained by adding together all the measurements for the characteristic and dividing this sum by the total number of such readings. The formula is

$$\bar{x} = \frac{\Sigma x}{n} \tag{1}$$

(*b*) Calculate the standard deviation s of the measurements for the sample. The standard deviation is a measure of the variability of individual measurements around the average or mean value. In precise terms it is the square root of the sum of the squares of departures of individual values from the mean after this sum is divided by one less than the number of items in the sample. The formula is

$$s = \sqrt{\frac{\Sigma (x - \bar{x})^2}{n - 1}} \tag{2}$$

For computation, a more useful formula is

$$s = \sqrt{\frac{n \Sigma x^2 - (\Sigma x)^2}{n(n - 1)}} \tag{3}$$

The computing can be arranged according to a method given in the Appendix to show whether or not the acceptance criterion has been met without computing either the mean or the standard deviation explicitly. The principal difficulty encountered in a direct application of the acceptance criterion by the methods shown in this section is the calculation of the standard deviation. However, this difficulty is undoubtedly exaggerated by persons with little or no experience in computation with short-cut procedures and modern computing machines.

Use of the basic formula (2) for determining the standard deviation requires the explicit calculation of departures from the mean and the squaring of such values. This step introduces inaccuracies and requires unnecessary work. For computation purposes, formula (3) should be used. The two quantities Σx^2 and Σx, required under this formula, can be computed simultaneously by using one of the standard calculating machines or a table of squares. The quantity Σx can be used also in the computation of the mean.

(*c*) Apply the acceptance criterion. A value for a constant k is given by the single-sample variables plan being applied, and a specification limit is assumed to have been established. If the specification limit is an upper limit, represented by U, and if the sample mean $\bar{x}$ plus k times the sample standard deviation s is equal to or less than ($\leq$) U, the lot is acceptable for this quality characteristic.   If the mean plus k times the standard deviation is greater than the specification limit, the lot should be rejected.   These statements hold true only for the case where the specification is an upper limit.   The formula for the acceptance criterion with U an upper limit is

$$\bar{x} + ks \leq U \tag{4}$$

If the quality specification is a minimum measurement, the criterion for acceptance is that the sample mean minus k times the sample standard deviation be equal to or greater than L, this lower limit.   The formula for the acceptance criterion with L a lower limit is

$$\bar{x} - ks \geq L \tag{5}$$

If criterion (4) or (5), whichever is appropriate, cannot be met, the lot is rejected; in the long run the percentage of defective items in such lots will be greater than the percentage one expects to receive under the selected plan.   The procedure given in this section is repeated for each measured property of the item, using the appropriate inspection data, specification limits, and inspection plans.   When a product is inspected for several characteristics, each one must meet its acceptance criterion for the lot to be accepted; if any one is not met, the lot must be rejected.

For some lots the sample mean $\bar{x}$ may approach the specification limit very closely and perhaps exceed the item limit if it is an upper limit U or fall short of the limit if it is a lower one L.   In such cases, one can see without further calculations that the lot will not meet the acceptance criterion; the calculation of the standard deviation will be necessary only if a process average is to be determined.   (The process average and its use is discussed in Secs. 6 and 7.)

For installations in which a particular sampling plan is to be used for a great many lots, an acceptance criterion for single sampling may be used which does not require the calculation of the standard deviation, but only the sum and the sum of squares of the measurements.   Details of this criterion and the methods for its use are given in the Appendix.

4.2. Calculations for Double-sample Plans

Under plans based on the drawing of two samples from the lot, the calculations are of the same nature as those for single-sample plans but are a little more extensive.   The following is an outline of the steps in the double-sampling procedure.   In the discussion, U again represents an upper specification limit and L a lower limit for the item characteristic being measured.

(a) Calculate the mean $\bar{x}_1$ of the measurements for items in the first sample. Double sampling requires the drawing of a relatively small "first" sample from the lot. For very good or very bad lots, this is the only sample which will have to be taken; for the other lots in between, a second sample must be drawn to reach a decision. Let n_1 represent the number of items specified by the plan for the first sample and x_1 represent the measurement of the given characteristic for any one item in this first sample. Then

$$\bar{x}_1 = \frac{\Sigma x_1}{n_1} \tag{6}$$

(b) Calculate the standard deviation s_1 of the measurements for items in the first sample. In terms of the formula that is most useful for computation, this is

$$s_1 = \sqrt{\frac{n_1 \Sigma x_1^2 - (\Sigma x_1)^2}{n_1(n_1 - 1)}} \tag{7}$$

(c) Apply a first-sample acceptance criterion. The value for a factor k_a is obtained from the selected sampling plan. This value is used to form an acceptance criterion which will take one of the two following forms, depending on whether the specification is an upper or a lower limit. The acceptance criterion with U an upper limit is

$$\bar{x}_1 + k_a s_1 \leq U \tag{8}$$

With U an upper limit, accept the lot if the first-sample mean plus k_a times the first-sample standard deviation is equal to or less than the limit U. The acceptance criterion with L a lower limit is

$$\bar{x}_1 - k_a s_1 \geq L \tag{9}$$

With L a lower limit, the criterion for acceptance is that the first-sample mean minus k_a times the first-sample standard deviation be equal to or greater than L.

If the appropriate one of the acceptance criteria is met, the lot is acceptable in so far as this item characteristic is concerned. Steps (a), (b), and (c) are then repeated on the other measurements if more than one property of the item is inspected. If acceptability is indicated each time, the lot is accepted without further calculations and without taking a second sample. On the other hand, if the acceptance criterion is not met by any one defect, the lot cannot be accepted on evidence from the first sample.

(d) Apply a first-sample rejection criterion. When a lot is not accepted by the steps above, data from the first sample is then tested for possible evidence that the lot should be rejected. For doing this, a value for a second constant k_r is furnished by the sampling plans. The two criteria for rejection take these forms: the rejection criterion with U an upper limit is

$$\bar{x}_1 + k_r s_1 \geq U \qquad (10)$$

the rejection criterion with L a lower limit is

$$\bar{x}_1 - k_r s_1 \leq L \qquad (11)$$

If the appropriate one of the above criteria is met for any one defect the lot is rejected without further consideration.

To summarize, a lot is accepted on evidence from the first sample if it passes the acceptance criteria for each possible defect; it is rejected if it meets a rejection criterion for any one of the possible defects.

If neither acceptance nor rejection is indicated by these first-sample calculations, a decision is deferred pending the drawing of another sample. Evidence from this second sample added to the evidence from the first one will then be adequate to reach a final decision on the disposal of the lot. The steps outlined next must be taken for lots that do require a second sample.

(e) Draw a second sample from the lot and measure each item. The sample size for this second sample will be indicated by the sampling plan in use. In this discussion, the number of items it contains is represented by n_2. A measurement of the given characteristic for any one item will be represented by x_2.

(f) Calculate the mean $\bar{x}_t$ for measurements from the first and second samples combined. It should be noted that, after a second sample has been drawn and its items measured, all calculations use data from the first and second samples combined. The mean for the combined samples $\bar{x}_t$ is given by the formula

$$\bar{x}_t = \frac{\Sigma x_1 + \Sigma x_2}{n_1 + n_2} \qquad (12)$$

(g) Calculate the standard deviation s_t for measurements from the first and second samples combined. The formula for obtaining this value by use of the sum of the measurements and the sum of the squares of the measurements is

$$s_t = \sqrt{\frac{(n_1 + n_2)(\Sigma x_1^2 + \Sigma x_2^2) - (\Sigma x_1 + \Sigma x_2)^2}{(n_1 + n_2)(n_1 + n_2 - 1)}} \qquad (13)$$

(h) Apply an acceptance criterion for combined samples. For this step, the value for a third constant k_t is specified by the sampling plan.

Again the criteria take familiar forms. The acceptance criterion for combined samples with U an upper limit is

$$\bar{x}_t + k_t s_t \leq U \qquad (14)$$

The acceptance criterion for combined samples with L a lower limit is

$$\bar{x}_t - k_t s_t \geq L \qquad (15)$$

If the appropriate one of these criteria is met, the lot is acceptable for the characteristic being considered. If the lot is found acceptable for each possible defect, it is accepted. If the criterion is not met for any one, the lot is rejected. Thus, through these calculations which follow the taking of a second sample, a final decision on the disposal of the lot is always made.

5. OPTIONAL FORMS FOR THE CRITERIA

It seemed most straightforward and perhaps most useful for the criteria under variables inspection to be in the form as used above, but there are many alternative methods. No one method is inherently superior for all inspection situations; the choice will depend largely on the nature of the data, the number and spacing of inspection lots, and the personnel and computing equipment available. In case there are large numbers of lots being presented in a continuous sequence, efficiency in the routine application of the variables plans will warrant relatively more attention than when a variety of working conditions are encountered. An Appendix has been included the purpose of which is to suggest to the inspection administrator some of the possibilities for carrying out the calculations in routine applications more easily.

Five different schemes for applying the one-sided acceptance criteria to the sample data of individual lots are presented. For simplicity, all the methods are discussed in relation to single sampling. However, the application to double sampling is completely analogous. The five methods are:

1. Standard method
2. Optional form for standard criteria
3. Difference method
4. Quadratic method
   a. Analytic
   b. Graphical
5. Squared-difference method
   a. Analytic
   b. Graphical

The first three methods require the calculation of $\bar{x}$, the sample mean, and s, the sample standard deviation from the sums Σx and Σx^2, whereas under the last two methods $\bar{x}$ and s need not be determined explicitly, Σx and Σx^2 being used instead. The advantages of using a method requiring the computation of $\bar{x}$ and s are the ease in the interpretation of sampling results, particularly if inspection lots are infrequent, and the availability of data in a form suitable for control purposes. The advantage of using a method that does not require computing $\bar{x}$ and s is the saving of time in the calculations for each lot. In particular, no dividing need be done and no square roots need be extracted.

In addition to the analytic methods of applying the test criteria, graphic methods may be employed. Some initial work is necessary for an application, but since under a graphical solution there is a possibility of eliminating one or more of the routine computational steps, it may be justified under some methods of applying the acceptance criteria when many lots are to be inspected. For those interested, a graphical procedure is described in the Appendix for each of the methods under which this form of solution may at times be worth while.

For applications in which the number of lots under a particular plan are expected to be few or are expected to be presented at infrequent intervals, the choice of method to be used in analyzing the sample data and in applying the acceptance criteria may be of minor economic importance. This will be particularly true in cases where the cost of inspecting an item is relatively great. Thus for many situations in which these variables plans are most valuable, the question of efficiency in the calculations is a secondary matter. However, in any case, once a technique has been established, the computation time required for any lot should not be more than a few minutes.

6. COMPUTATION OF PROCESS AVERAGES

In the use of sampling inspection plans, it is usually well to determine what the average quality of product recently submitted has been. This information will be useful in at least two ways. First, an estimate of recent incoming quality will give, through the OC curve for the sampling plan, a rough estimate of the quality of lots that have been accepted. This information may have general value to management, perhaps in evaluating, for example, the quality of their own product in which the purchased material has been used. Second, such information may have an important and specific use in determining what sampling plan to use for acceptance inspection in the immediate future. As pointed out in the previous chapter, the proper selection of a sampling plan depends on an estimate of what submitted quality will be. The receiver should change to another plan when information gained from product actually inspected indicates a percent defective differing considerably from the percentage expected.

The complete procedure for the selection and use of these variables plans, just as under the corresponding attribute plans, calls for the computation of a "process average" as a measure of what incoming quality has been. This part of the procedure may be omitted if one can get in other ways an estimate of incoming quality or can determine that the sampling plan in use is giving the desired amount of protection.

The true percentage of defects in submitted product cannot be found when inspection is by sampling. However, calculating the process average does give a close estimate. The accuracy of this estimate will, in general, depend on the total number of items used in the calculations.

In finding the process average for a product, measurements of sample items from a series of consecutive inspection lots are used. Both accepted and rejected lots are included. (However, data from any lot produced under conditions known to be abnormal should be excluded.) If a double-sample plan has been used, only measurements from first samples are used. The series of lots should be long enough to give a total of at least three hundred sample items and preferably more. However, no rules exist for determining closely the number of sample items that should be used; the number will depend on how accurate the estimate must be of the quality of recently submitted lots. The number will depend, too, on how much inspection data is available. If there is considerable uncertainty about the submitted quality of a new product or of an old product from a new supplier, a preliminary process average should be calculated fairly soon, even though relatively few items have been measured. The number of lots included will depend, too, on the AQL class, the number required being less the greater the percent defective. One additional point should be mentioned; the series of lots should, if at all possible, be unbroken in so far as time of production is concerned. Measurements from lots recently produced and shipped should not be combined with measurements from a series of lots produced and shipped a long time ago. The process average helps in choosing the most appropriate sampling plan by giving some idea of the quality that is apt to be submitted in the future. The quality of product most recently shipped is likely to be the most dependable guide.

A process average is found by considering the run of recently submitted lots as one grand lot and considering the sum of the samples from these lots as one grand sample. The mean $\bar{\bar{x}}$ and the standard deviation $\bar{\bar{s}}$ are calculated for the measurements from this group of samples, or grand sample, and used as estimates for the mean and standard deviation for the grand lot. With this estimate of the mean and standard deviation, an estimate of the percent defective in the grand lot can be obtained, just as an estimate of the quality of a single inspection lot can be obtained from its sample mean and sample standard deviation. This estimate of the proportion defective for the grand lot is called the "process average."

One might use directly the measurements for items in each lot sample to calculate the mean and standard deviation for this grand sample. However, the required values $\bar{\bar{x}}$ and $\bar{\bar{s}}$ can be obtained more easily through use of each lot mean $\bar{x}$ and lot standard deviation s or through use of the sum of the measurements Σx and the sum of the squares of the measurements Σx^2 for each sample as they were calculated when the lots were submitted to the inspection procedure. Two recommended methods using these values are described below.

The first method is to apply the procedures used in computing the sample mean and sample standard deviation to values for the sums of measurements Σx and sums of the squares of measurements Σx^2 as determined for the sample from each lot. When these values are available, this method will be preferable.

The mean of the measurements from all the samples $\bar{\bar{x}}$ may be obtained by adding together the sum of the measurements as obtained for each sample and dividing this grand total of the measurements by the number of items in the combined samples. The formula is

$$\bar{\bar{x}} = \frac{\Sigma(\Sigma x)}{N} \tag{16}$$

where
$$N = \Sigma n \tag{17}$$

The standard deviation of the measurements $\bar{\bar{s}}$ may be obtained by the formula

$$\bar{\bar{s}} = \sqrt{\frac{N\Sigma(\Sigma x^2) - [\Sigma(\Sigma x)]^2}{N(N-1)}} \tag{18}$$

When the sample sums are not available, $\bar{\bar{x}}$ and $\bar{\bar{s}}$ may be computed by a second method from the sample means and sample standard deviations for the series of lots.

If the sample size n is the same from lot to lot, as will almost always be the case, the following formulas apply:

$$\bar{\bar{x}} = \frac{n}{N} \Sigma \bar{x} \tag{19}$$

and
$$\bar{\bar{s}} = \sqrt{\frac{(n-1)\Sigma s^2 + n\Sigma \bar{x}^2 - (n^2/N)(\Sigma \bar{x})^2}{N-1}} \tag{20}$$

For the exceptional case where sample sizes are not the same, the following formulas may be used:

$$\bar{\bar{x}} = \frac{\sum\limits_{i=1}^{m} n_i \bar{x}_i}{N} \tag{21}$$

and

$$\bar{\bar{s}} = \sqrt{\frac{\sum\limits_{i=1}^{m} (n_i - 1)s_i^2 + \sum\limits_{i=1}^{m} n_i \bar{x}_i^2 - \left(\sum\limits_{i=1}^{m} n_i \bar{x}_i\right)^2 / N}{N - 1}} \tag{22}$$

where n_i = the number of observations in the ith sample

$N = \Sigma n_i$

$\bar{x}_i$ = the mean of the ith sample

s_i = the standard deviation of the ith sample

m = the number of samples

The second part of the procedure is the actual determination of the process average through the use of $\bar{\bar{x}}$ and $\bar{\bar{s}}$. This step is carried out by first obtaining a value designated as $\bar{k}$. This value is obtained when an upper limit is specified by subtracting $\bar{\bar{x}}$ from U, the upper specification limit, and dividing the result by $\bar{\bar{s}}$. The formula is

$$\bar{k} = \frac{U - \bar{\bar{x}}}{\bar{\bar{s}}} \tag{23}$$

If the specification is a lower limit L, $\bar{k}$ is obtained by subtracting L from $\bar{\bar{x}}$ and dividing the result by $\bar{\bar{s}}$. The formula is

$$\bar{k} = \frac{\bar{\bar{x}} - L}{\bar{\bar{s}}} \tag{24}$$

The value obtained for $\bar{k}$ is then taken into Chart G, which gives directly an estimate of the percent defective for the grand lot—the process average.

When only a rough approximation is desired, one possibility is to compute the process average on an attribute basis. This can be done by first reviewing the measurements from items in each sample and noting how many fall beyond the specifications limit and thus represent defective items. The total number of such actual defectives in all the samples from the grand lot divided by the total number of sample items will give the average percent defective. This method, since item quality has been considered on an attribute basis, will not ordinarily give a value so close to the true process average as the recommended procedure, but the calculations are considerably simpler.

If the item is inspected for several characteristics, a process average must be calculated for each one. When several suppliers are submitting a material to the same sampling plan, a separate average should usually be calculated for each, since there is almost certain to be some difference in quality among them.

Ordinarily a process average for a product should be calculated shortly after the start of acceptance inspection under a sampling plan in order to determine whether or not the plan in use is appropriate for the incoming quality level. Thereafter the average should be calculated at any time a noticeable increase or decrease in the proportion of lots rejected indicates an appreciable shift in the incoming quality level or when a shift in level is indicated in other ways. In the absence of any sign of change in incoming quality, the process average should be calculated just often enough to give assurance that the incoming product is actually at or near the quality one expects.

7. DETERMINATION OF WHETHER TIGHTENED OR REDUCED INSPECTION SHOULD BE APPLIED

The degree of protection given by a sampling plan depends to a great extent on the quality of submitted product. One of the early steps in the selection and installation of a plan is to estimate what the quality level of incoming product will probably be. If the expected level is equal to or better than the percentage defective that can reasonably be used, an AQL is ordinarily chosen close to this preliminary estimate. The use of a plan selected by this practice will give the expected protection only if the preliminary estimate of incoming quality will be near the actual figure.

Calculation of the process average gives a much closer estimate of submitted quality than can be obtained in other ways; it gives an estimate from which one can be reasonably sure of selecting an appropriate sampling plan. For this reason, calculating a process average after the initial period of receiving a product is recommended. Furthermore, the average quality of submitted product may shift from time to time, so that the plan in current use may no longer be appropriate. Hence, as part of the procedure, a process average is calculated periodically. If it is found to be close to the AQL for the plan in use, acceptance inspection can be continued using this plan. However, if the process average shows incoming product to be considerably worse than the selected AQL, a change to another plan is essential; if the process average shows incoming product considerably better than the selected AQL, a change may be desirable.

Sampling plans are not certain in their action; some lots with a percent defective above the AQL will be accepted. If the general run of incoming lots is somewhat worse than the selected AQL, a few of them will be passed.   If the selected AQL represents the lowest quality level that can reasonably be used, normal operation under the plan will not give adequate protection.   Under such circumstances, "tightened inspection" will be necessary.   Tightened inspection will reject a much larger percentage of unacceptable lots than will normal inspection and thus give a closer approach under such circumstances to the required acceptance protection.   Furthermore, the rejection of a higher percentage of lots will furnish an added incentive for the supplier to improve the quality of the product he submits.

On the other hand, the process average may indicate a submitted quality better than the selected AQL.   A process average lower than the AQL indicates that relatively few unacceptable lots are being submitted and so one need not rely so much on the sampling plan.   Under such conditions it may be advisable to go on "reduced inspection."   Reduced inspection calls for smaller samples than normal inspection and for this reason reduces inspection costs.

To assist in reaching a decision on whether or not to place a product on tightened inspection or to place it on reduced inspection, reference is made to Table H.   This table gives upper and lower limits for process averages for each AQL class under which these variables plans are classified.   After calculating a process average, it is carried into the table under the AQL range for the plan in use and on the horizontal line corresponding to the total number of items in the samples used in obtaining the average.   If the calculated value falls between the indicated limits, this is reasonable assurance that incoming quality has been close to the selected AQL.   When this does happen, normal inspection should be continued.

One should note that, in Table H, the limits for process averages are considerably wider than the range of the corresponding AQL class.   Since a process average is determined from sample data, it may vary somewhat from the true value.   These limits have been placed far enough apart to care for this variation in all but the occasional extreme case.   One may note also, when examining the table, how this allowance for possible error in the process average diminishes as the number of sample items used in its calculation increases.   For the very large grand lot, the probable range in values is but little greater than the AQL class.

8. TIGHTENED INSPECTION

Sometimes presented quality may be such that the process average does not fall between the appropriate limits in the table.   It may fall, for example, above the upper limit.   When this happens, presented quality is almost certainly worse than the selected AQL; either the preliminary estimate of what incoming quality would be was too low (if the process average covered the initial period of use for a plan), or there has been a recent drop in the supplier's quality. Either situation requires tightened inspection if the quality of accepted product is to be maintained close to the selected level.

Tightened inspection is put into effect by using a value for k in single sampling or values for k_a, k_r, and k_t in double sampling taken from an AQL class two classes lower than the one selected for normal inspection. The sample-size letter used in normal inspection is retained. This change in the procedure can be easily made by using the complete collection of plans in Table E or by using the summaries of the plans in Tables B and C.

Using a k from an AQL class two classes lower increases the magnitude of k and thus stiffens the acceptance criteria. In this way tightened inspection gives the necessary increase in protection and, since the sample size is not increased, gives it without increasing inspection costs. For the occasional case where the lowest or next to lowest AQL class available in this collection of plans is in use for normal inspection, tightened inspection will have to be put into effect by using the next higher inspection level instead of selecting a value of k from a lower AQL class.

A process average must be calculated for each quality characteristic measured and a separate comparison made in Table H with each appropriate AQL. Tightened inspection is put into effect for only those defects whose process average falls above its upper limit. Thus, a product may be submitted to normal inspection for some defects and to tightened inspection for others.

Tightened inspection is continued for a defect until a newly calculated process average shows definite improvement. When the submitted product improves in quality to such an extent that the new process average has a value equal to or less than the larger figure defining the desired AQL class, normal inspection may be resumed. One should carefully note that this criterion for resuming normal inspection is the upper figure defining the desired AQL class and not the upper limit for process averages listed under that class in Table H. Use of the upper side of the AQL class makes it more difficult to return to normal inspection than it was to leave it. The procedure intends to make it more difficult to return, so that there will not be frequent changes between normal and tightened inspection during periods when the quality level of submitted product is running just a little worse than the desired AQL class. The nature of this criterion for returning to normal inspection sometimes causes tightened inspection to be continued for awhile after incoming product becomes satisfactory. It will not continue very long, however, if the supplier has made an adequate improvement in quality.

9. REDUCED INSPECTION

The other possibility when comparing the process average with the selected AQL is that the average may fall below the lower limit shown in the table. If it does, this is good evidence that incoming product is considerably better than the AQL. Under such a circumstance, less protection is needed, so "reduced inspection" may be inaugurated.

To establish reduced inspection, an inspection level one level lower than the one for normal inspection is used. Since level II is used for normal inspection in most installations, reduced inspection usually calls for the use of inspection level I. The AQL class for normal inspection is retained. The use of a lower level calls for a lower sample-size letter; this reduces the size of the sample, which, in turn, gives the desired end effect of reduced acceptance inspection costs.

Since changing to reduced inspection lowers the protection offered by the acceptance procedure, it must be done with considerable caution. The following criteria have been established, all of which should be met before this change is made:

(a) The process average for each possible defect in the product must be low enough to fall below the appropriate lower limit for process averages as established in Table H. If any one defect does not meet this test, normal inspection must be continued for all defects.

(b) The last 20 inspection lots submitted under normal inspection must all have been accepted.

(c) The production and submission of the item must be fairly continuous. When there are indications that production is not continuous or when purchases of the item are made at infrequent intervals, reduced inspection should not be used. Under such conditions, data from the last lots inspected may not be a reliable indication of future quality.

When operating under reduced inspection, normal inspection must be resumed at once if any one of the following three things happen:

(a) An inspection lot is rejected through operation of the sampling plan.

(b) The process average for any one defect becomes large enough so that it exceeds the upper value limiting the selected AQL class. One should note that it is the upper number defining the AQL class which is used in this criterion and not the upper limit for process averages as given in Table H.

(c) The production or purchase of the item has been interrupted for a considerable period of time.

The recommended procedure is for normal inspection to be resumed for all quality characteristics. Since normal inspection for one characteristic would call for larger sample sizes, little would be gained in situations where reduced inspection might be retained for some of the item characteristics.

10. SELECTION AND OPERATION OF PLANS IN TERMS OF THE AOQL

The possibility of screening rejected inspection lots and including them with the accepted lots was discussed in Sec. 3 of Chap. 3. If the screening is done well enough to remove all the defectives, the average quality of accepted product, including the screened lots, can be computed. As shown in Sec. 3.4 of Chap. 3, this quality of accepted product, the average outgoing quality (AOQ), has a limit, the average outgoing-quality limit (AOQL), for each plan. This limit represents the maximum percentage of defective items, on the average, in product finally accepted, under the condition that rejected inspection lots be screened and returned with no defects, regardless of the quality originally submitted. In practice, the AOQL is approached only when submitted quality is somewhat worse than the AQL for the plan. But if product is submitted whose quality level is equal to or better than the AQL, the average quality of outgoing product will usually be much better than that indicated by the AOQL of the sampling plan.

For some installations, selection of a sampling plan in terms of the AOQL may be desirable. If it is very important that the percentage of defective items does not exceed some maximum figure, selection of a plan on an AOQL basis will assure this requirement being met in the long run. Or, if product is produced or purchased at infrequent intervals, acceptance inspection on this basis is particularly desirable. However, it should be noted that the choice of a plan on an AOQL basis can be made only when rejected lots are screened and returned with all defective items replaced by perfect items. Therefore, use of an AOQL in choosing a sampling plan must be done carefully, since these variables plans will be applied most often to products for which screening is not feasible, that is, to products on which measurements are difficult to make or to products which are destroyed by inspection.

An AOQL class in percent defective is given for each of these variables plans. In selecting a plan, the AOQL class containing the desired AOQL is determined. Each AOQL class will be found under several sample-size letters and for some letters may be found under two AQL classes. The next step is to select from the several plans available for an AOQL class the one that will operate most satisfactorily. Some assistance in making a choice may be obtained through Table I, which summarizes sample-size letters available for each AOQL class and subgroups them by AQL classes. On first thought it might seem best to select the lowest sample-size letter available, since this would require the least amount of sampling inspection. However, in many cases, a selection on this basis might result in the rejection of an unnecessarily large percentage of submitted lots, which would have to be screened. A choice more satisfactory to both the supplier and the receiver will be obtained if one chooses, instead, the lowest sample-size letter in an AQL class that is close to the estimate of what the quality of submitted product will be.

• After a plan has been selected, inspection under it is performed just as it is when selection is in terms of an AQL. The steps for the calculation of process averages and the attendant changes to reduced or tightened inspection can be omitted. Care must be taken, of course, to see that all rejected lots have been screened properly and have been marked so that they may be identified and properly handled upon their return.

11. CURTAILED INSPECTION

Sometimes the inspector may note, before measuring all of the items in a sample, that the lot cannot possibly be accepted or may note that undoubtedly it will be accepted. Through experience with operation under the plan, he may be certain, for example, that all the readings taken so far are running too high or that the number of readings actually above the specification limit is too great for the lot to pass the acceptance criterion. Or, if the product is inspected for two or more properties, it may be that measurements from the first property checked show that the lot must be rejected. When it becomes obvious to the inspector that a lot will or will not be accepted, it may seem desirable to curtail inspection, that is, to make no more measurements and no more calculations.

Curtailing inspection may seem to be a means of reducing inspection time and labor and thus be desirable from a cost standpoint. If the sole objective in inspecting a sample is to determine the disposal of the lot, curtailed inspection might well be practiced. However, it is almost always necessary, for reasons given in previous sections, to have a close estimate of current incoming quality—the process average. A correct process average will probably not be secured through ordinary procedures if inspection is curtailed; extremely poor lots or extremely good lots will not be fully represented in the calculations, and thus a misleading figure will be obtained.

12. COMBINED VARIABLES AND ATTRIBUTE PLANS

It may be desirable to formulate a sampling inspection scheme utilizing both variables and attribute plans. Such a scheme may operate in the following manner: A sample is taken and subjected to a variables test of the form $\bar{x} + ks \le U$ (or $\bar{x} - ks \ge L$). The lot is accepted if the test criterion $\bar{x} + ks \le U$ is satisfied. However, if acceptance is not indicated, a second sample is taken and the number of defectives counted. If the number of defective items does not exceed a given acceptance number, the lot is accepted; otherwise it is rejected.

This procedure is appropriate if the receiver is in doubt as to whether incoming product has been screened, since in the combined plan, for a lot to be rejected, at least one defective item must be found in the sample. As a matter of fact, whether the lot has been screened or not, many suppliers object to the rejection of lots on the basis of samples which do not contain defective items.

Various types of combined plans are available. For example, the attribute criterion may be applied only to the second sample or it may be applied to the first and second samples combined. In this book, only the defectives in the second sample will be used in the attribute test because the OC curve of such a plan is simple to compute. The procedure is as follows: A first-sample variables plan is chosen from the comprehensive listing given in Table B. This plan is chosen so that the OC curve for the combined plan is satisfactory. Directions for computing this combined OC curve are given below. A first sample is drawn of size n, and the lot is accepted if the variables criterion is satisfied, that is, if $\bar{x} + ks \le U$ (or if $\bar{x} - ks \ge L$). If acceptance is not indicated, a second sample of size $3n/2$ is taken and inspected for defective items. If no defects are found in the $3n/2$ items, the lot is accepted; if one or more defects are found, the lot is rejected. Inspection of the second sample may be curtailed as soon as a defective item is found. In this case, the lot is rejected.

The addition of an attribute plan to one of the standard variables plans will result in an OC curve which lies above the OC curve of the variables plan when used alone. No comprehensive set of OC curves is given for testing with the combined plans. However, directions are given for the computation of the OC curve for the combined plan outlined in the preceding paragraph. For any variables plan the probability that the plan will accept a lot characterized by a given proportion defective can be determined from the curves in Table E. Denote this probability by $P(A_1)$. The probability of accepting under the attribute plan, $P(A_2)$ say, is given by Chart O. The OC curve for the combined plan is given by $P(A_1) + [1 - P(A_1)]P(A_2)$. The method of computation is illustrated by the following example.

Suppose that the variables plan chosen is sample-size letter **J**, AQL class 1.2 to 2.2. Thus the first sample size is 60. We desire the probability of accepting under the combined plan for proportion defective of 0.02. Entering Table E and using Chart 2 for sample letter J, we read from curve 9 that for a percent defective of 2, 95 percent of lots will be accepted. (Note that the decimal point is moved two places to the right to convert from proportion defective to percent defective. Thus in this example, the probability of accepting a lot characterized by 0.02 proportion defective is 0.95.) For this plan, the second sample of $3n/2$ is equal to 90. Entering Chart O with a p of 0.02 and $3n/2$ of 90, $P(A_2)$ is found to equal 0.16. Thus the point on the desired OC curve corresponding to a p of 0.02 is $0.95 + (0.05)(0.16) = 0.9580$. This procedure is repeated for various values of p to construct the entire OC curve.

There is no hard-and-fast rule for choosing the variables plan so that the resulting OC curve will be satisfactory. However, since the computation of the OC curve for the combined plan is simple, various plans can be tried. In trial calculations, it is usually necessary to consider only two points, the AQL and the LTPD. If the OC curve at these points gives the desired protection, the plan is usually satisfactory.

CHAPTER 6

PLANS FOR USE WHEN THE STANDARD DEVIATION OF THE PRODUCT IS KNOWN

1. FIELD OF USE FOR THESE PLANS

For many industrial products, the mean of the measurements of item characteristics changes from lot to lot while the dispersion of the measurements about the means do not change appreciably, so that the standard deviations remain practically constant. This occurs because, for many manufacturing processes, the relatively important or assignable causes of item variation that enter to produce noticeable changes affect only the average diameter, the average length, the average hardness or the average of other properties. For example, this is commonly the effect of such assignable causes as the slippage of machine adjustments, incorrect tool or machine settings, or pronounced tool wear. The dispersions of measurements about their mean value, on the other hand, will be produced by the constantly present system of minor chance-acting causes inherent in the process—a system that will remain approximately the same regardless of any change in the mean and so will keep the standard deviation almost constant. Under such circumstances, the value for the standard deviation can be accurately estimated from sample data and used in quality control procedures.

The basic variables plans discussed in the preceding chapters and presented in Table E assume that either the mean of item measurements or the standard deviation or both may change from lot to lot and so are designed to care for sampling errors in both these lot properties. If, on the other hand, the standard deviation of a product is known so that one need assume that only the mean may vary, less allowance has to be made in the plans for sampling error. Consequently, the sample need not contain so many items as the sample for a comparable plan for use where the standard deviation is not known. For this reason it was worth while to design plans for products whose standard deviation is known. Successful applications of such plans have been made.†

† See Paul C. Clifford, "Acceptance Sampling Inspection by Variables," *Industrial Quality Control*, Vol. 3, No. 5, pp. 12–15, March, 1947; Paul Peach, "An Introduction to Industrial Statistics and Quality Control," 2d ed., Chap. VIII, Edwards and Broughton Company, Raleigh, N.C., 1947; H. F. Dodge, "Statistical Control in Sampling Inspection," *American Machinist*, Vol. 76, pp. 1085–1088, 1129–1131, Oct. 26 and Nov. 9, 1932.

Under variables inspection, known-sigma plans may be designed to make acceptance depend on a satisfactory mean for the measurements or designed to make acceptance depend on the estimated number of defective items in the lot being an acceptable quantity. The known-sigma plans presented here use the latter form of criterion; for the same reasons as given in the discussion under the unknown-sigma plans, the lot is evaluated in terms of the percent of items defective.

2. SAVINGS IN THE USE OF KNOWN-SIGMA PLANS

The reductions in sample sizes for known-sigma plans under those for unknown-sigma plans are appreciable, particularly for the larger sample sizes. Some idea of the savings in inspection costs from the use of smaller samples may be obtained by examining Table 6.1, which shows for single-

TABLE 6.1.   SAVINGS IN SINGLE-SAMPLE SIZE UNDER KNOWN-SIGMA VARIABLES PLANS

Sample-size letter	Sample size under unknown-sigma plans	Sample size under known-sigma plans	Savings	
			Actual	Percentage
B	7	5	2	29
C	10	6	4	40
D	13	7	6	46
E	16	9	7	44
F	20	11	9	45
G	25	13	12	48
H	35	16	19	54
I	50	20	30	60
J	60	24	36	60
K	70	28	42	60
L	85	32	53	62
M	100	36	64	64
N	125	40	85	68
O	200	45	155	78

sampling the sample sizes for both types of plans together with the savings under the known-sigma form.

In addition to the significant savings from reduced sample sizes, another advantage in the use of these plans is that the standard deviation does not have to be calculated for the sample from each lot. This reduces the necessary clerical work considerably. Once the product standard deviation has been determined, the principal calculations remaining are the relatively simple ones for finding the average of the measurements for the sample from each lot.

In connection with this last point one precaution should be made. When sampling inspection is by variables, there may be an inclination to use the more familiar unknown-sigma plans for goods whose standard deviation is known but to reduce clerical work by discontinuing the calculation of the sample standard deviation for each lot. This might be done by determining the average sample standard deviation $\bar{s}$ for past lots and using this value in the acceptance criterion for future lots instead of the sample standard deviation s as ordinarily used. The above practices, if followed, will make the sampling plan considerably more stringent in its action than its AQL and OC curve indicate. From an administrative standpoint it will be preferable to use the plans described in this chapter so that the degree of protection actually being achieved will be known. Also, under use of the known-sigma plans additional savings from reduced sample sizes can be realized. When used in this way, as part of a standard acceptance inspection procedure, the known-sigma plans offer an alternative to going on reduced inspection under an unknown-sigma plan. Using a known-sigma plan requires an accurate estimate of sigma based on past data so that this estimate may be used as a constant in the procedure without losing any protection under the given sampling plans. Similarly, changing to a reduced inspection program under an unknown-sigma plan is done after inspecting past performance and observing that the incoming production is satisfactory and stable enough to allow the reduction in sample size. Therefore, the two procedures—using a known-sigma plan and going on reduced inspection with the unknown-sigma plan—are both similar in their inspection for constancy of past production performance.

3. DETERMINATION OF THE PRODUCT STANDARD DEVIATION

These plans assume that an accurate estimate of the lot standard deviation for each measured characteristic will be available. Since it is unlikely in ordinary situations that this information will specifically be known on a lot-by-lot basis for items to be submitted in the future, the practical implication of this underlying assumption is that the standard deviation is in control—that its value will virtually be constant from lot to lot. The procedure assumes that a reliable estimate will be made of its value and that this estimate will then be used in the acceptance criterion for future incoming goods as the standard deviation for the items of each inspection lot.

The estimate of the standard deviation must be reasonably accurate for the plans to give the protection indicated by their AQL. In effect, this usually means, first of all, that control charts for s, the sample standard deviation, must be maintained for each measured characteristic for some time prior to a change to these plans. Procedures for setting up control charts for s are outlined in Sec. 4 of Chap. 9. If the charts show that the dispersion of item measurements about their average has been in control, then it will be feasible to predict the standard deviation for future submitted lots.   The charts will serve not only to determine the presence or absence of control but also to find the value of sigma.   An estimate of sigma may be made from $\bar{s}$, the value of the center line on the control chart for s, by procedures that are outlined in Chap. 9, Sec. 4.

The degree of accuracy needed in the estimate of sigma depends on three factors: (1) on the sample-size letter or sample size, (2) on the AQL class, and (3) on whether the value is underestimated or over-estimated.   Some idea of the effect of using an inaccurate estimate of sigma can be obtained from Table 6.2, which shows for a representative

TABLE 6.2.   THE EFFECT OF ERROR IN THE ESTIMATE OF SIGMA ON THE PERCENTAGE OF SUBMITTED INSPECTION LOTS ACCEPTED WHEN INCOMING QUALITY IS AT THE AQL

Sample-size letter	AQL class	Percentage of incoming lots accepted						
		Overestimate			No error in estimate	Underestimate		
		10%	5%	1%		1%	5%	10%
C	0.32–0.65	90.05	92.92	94.63	95.00	95.35	96.57	97.70
	3.2 –4.4	91.24	93.32	94.69	95.00	95.29	96.32	97.34
F	0.32–0.65	87.54	91.90	94.47	95.00	95.49	97.07	98.37
	3.2 –4.4	88.95	92.42	94.55	95.00	95.42	96.82	98.06
	6.4 –8.5	90.15	92.89	94.62	95.00	95.36	96.58	97.72
J	0.12–0.17	75.01	87.70	93.92	95.00	95.92	98.34	99.55
	0.32–0.65	76.63	88.21	93.98	95.00	95.88	98.23	99.48
	3.2 –4.4	80.86	89.59	94.15	95.00	95.75	97.89	99.22
	6.4 –8.5	83.10	90.35	94.25	95.00	95.67	97.66	99.01
N	0.06–0.12	59.80	82.80	93.39	95.00	96.28	99.04	99.88
	0.22–0.32	61.00	83.20	93.43	95.00	96.26	99.00	99.87

selection of single-sampling plans the effect of different amounts of error on the percentage of submitted inspection lots that will be accepted when incoming quality is at the AQL.   Inspection of this table will show that an error of more than 1 percent can have an appreciable effect on the operating characteristics of a plan, particularly for the larger sample-size letters.

4. KNOWN-SIGMA PLANS

A set of plans for use under single sampling has been prepared for each combination of sample-size letter and AQL class covered by the plans for use where sigma is not known. Values for the single-sample size n' and for the constant k' used in the acceptance criterion are given in Table K. Also a set of plans for use under double sampling has been prepared for each combination covered by unknown-sigma double-sampling plans, with the exception of sample letters B and C for which no savings in double sampling over single sampling can be realized. The pertinent data for their operation, the first and second sample sizes, n'_1 and n'_2, respectively, and the constants k'_a, k'_r, k'_t are given in Table L.

A comparison of this table with Tables B and C, which summarize the plans for use when sigma is not known, will show that both the sample sizes and the constants have been changed. One possibility of constructing a set of related known-sigma plans would have been to retain the same constants but reduce the sample size. However, this would have required a different sample size for each AQL class under each sample-size letter, and in addition, the corresponding operating characteristic curves under both sets of plans would not have matched. To maintain a standard pattern of operation for all types of plans, one sample size was chosen for each sample-size letter to be used for all AQL classes covered by that letter, and new values were assigned to the constants—the values selected for sample sizes and constants being those giving operating characteristics matching most closely the related unknown-sigma plans.

Because the same sample size has been used throughout all AQL classes under a sample-size letter, the operating characteristics for these plans do not match exactly those for the unknown-sigma plans. A general knowledge of the differences between the two sets of plans can be obtained from Table M which lists side by side the corresponding AQL and LTPD for both sets of plans for single sampling.

The largest discrepancies occur in the values of the LTPD for the lower AQL classes for each sample-size letter. However, since in this region of the table the LTPD for unknown sigma is larger than the corresponding value for known sigma, the OC curve for known sigma is steeper and therefore the sampling plan is more stringent. If a receiver switches from an unknown-sigma plan to the corresponding known-sigma plan in the smaller AQL range, he is tightening his acceptance requirements somewhat. However, the reverse situation holds for the upper AQL classes, but it will be noticed that the discrepancies here are not so large as those for the lower AQL classes and do not occur in so wide a range of classes.

When more detailed knowledge of the operating characteristics of any specific plan is needed, its OC curve may be calculated easily. The curve may be constructed by determining for several assumed values of the proportion defective in incoming lots the percentage of lots in each case that will be accepted. The percentage of lots accepted plotted against the various assumed values of the proportion defective will give the OC curve. Two points on the curve are obtainable directly from Table M, the 95 percent point corresponding to the value of proportion defective equal to the AQL and the 10 percent point corresponding to a proportion defective equal to the LTPD. Values for other points on the curve may be obtained by the following procedure:

(1) Let p represent the proportion defective in incoming lots. Enter Chart G with this value, reading proportion defective p on the right side of the scale and obtain a corresponding reading on the left side of the scale. For use here, this reading will be called K_p.

(2) Compute

$$\sqrt{n'}\,(K_p - k') \tag{25}$$

where n' is the sample size and k' is the constant specified by the known-sigma plan being used.

(3) Reenter Chart G, this time reading on the left side of the scale the value obtained for $\sqrt{n'}\,(K_p - k')$. The corresponding value on the right of the scale will be the proportion of lots that will be accepted with p fraction defective in incoming lots. To obtain the percentage of incoming lots that will be accepted, move the decimal point two places to the right.

(4) Repeat steps (1), (2), and (3) for enough values of p to construct the OC curve.

The OC curves for the double-sampling known-sigma plans match the OC curves for their related single-sampling known-sigma plans. Since the OC curves for related single-sampling and double-sampling plans for use when sigma is not known match closely, the comparisons for single-sampling plans made in Table M or made by means of the OC curves derived from the formula above can be used to evaluate the protection given by double-sampling known-sigma plans.

5. INSTALLATION AND OPERATION OF THE PLANS

The selection of an AQL, the selection of an inspection level, and the other steps in the installation of a plan are performed in exactly the same manner as in the installation of plans for use when sigma is not known. Procedures outlined in Secs. 1 through 6 of Chap. 4 should be followed.

After a plan has been selected and installed, operations under it are essentially the same as for the unknown-sigma plans. The first three steps, the formation of inspection lots, the drawing of samples, and the inspection of items in the samples, are performed as specified in Secs. 1

to 3 of Chap. 5, using, of course, the sample sizes as specified for the known-sigma plans.

The next and final step—making the necessary calculations to determine the disposal of the lot—follows a modified pattern.   The principal difference is that s, the standard deviation for each lot, is not calculated; the value for σ, the product standard deviation, is used instead.   When circumstances make it desirable, however, a calculation to determine s may be made for plotting on a control chart or for the computation of a process average.

Formulas for the acceptance criteria take the basic form used in the other plans, but with the major change of using σ, the estimate of the lot standard deviation each time instead of s, the standard deviation for the sample.   Also, values for the constants are obtained from Table K or L instead of from Table B, C, or E.

With these changes, the formulas for the known-sigma criteria are as follows:

a. *Single Sampling.*   With U an upper limit, accept the lot if

$$\bar{x} + k'\sigma \leq U \tag{26}$$

With L a lower limit, accept the lot if

$$\bar{x} - k'\sigma \geq L \tag{27}$$

b. *Double Sampling*

1. *Criteria for the first sample.*   With U an upper limit, accept the lot if

$$\bar{x}_1 + k'_a\sigma \leq U \tag{28}$$

With L a lower limit, accept the lot if

$$\bar{x}_1 - k'_a\sigma \geq L \tag{29}$$

With U an upper limit, reject the lot if

$$\bar{x}_1 + k'_r\sigma \geq U \tag{30}$$

With L a lower limit, reject the lot if

$$\bar{x}_1 - k'_r\sigma \leq L \tag{31}$$

2. *Criteria for the second sample.*   With U an upper limit, accept the lot if

$$\bar{x}_t + k'_t\sigma \leq U \tag{32}$$

With L a lower limit, accept the lot if

$$\bar{x}_t - k'_t\sigma \geq L \tag{33}$$

6. TIGHTENED AND REDUCED INSPECTION

The procedure for the computation of a process average and for its use in determining whether to place a product on tightened or reduced inspection under a known-sigma plan is essentially the same as the procedure under an unknown-sigma plan as outlined in Secs. 6 to 9 of Chap. 5. However, the computation of a process average necessitates the calculation either of s or of the sum of the squared measurements, Σx^2, for each sample, although neither of these calculations is necessary for the acceptance criterion of the known-sigma plans. After the process average has been determined, its value is compared with the permissible limits for the process average as given in Table N for each AQL class and corresponding to the number of items on which the process average is based. If the calculated average falls within the limits, then, as in the unknown-sigma plans, normal inspection is continued. Procedures for the cases where the calculated process average falls outside the limits given in Table N are the same as those for unknown-sigma plans as stated in Secs. 8 and 9 of Chap. 5.

CHAPTER 7

PROCEDURES FOR TWO-SIDED SPECIFICATION LIMITS

1. THE FIELD FOR TWO-SIDED PLANS

For some products tested on a variables basis, an item may be unacceptable if one or more of its measured quality characteristics falls outside a specified range of allowable values. This range may be specified directly by giving maximum and minimum limits or indirectly by specifying a basic or nominal value and an allowable tolerance on either side. For example, such specifications are commonly applied to the diameters of shafts and bearings, to the more important dimensions of other metal parts finished by machine-tool operations, to the dimensions of stampings, forgings, and castings, and to some of the quality characteristics of condensers, resistors, and other component parts used in building electronic equipment.

Unfortunately, the mathematical theory behind the construction of unknown standard deviation variables plans for two-sided limits is not as straightforward as the theory behind one-sided plans, and the details of applying the procedures are more complicated. Therefore no attempt has been made to provide a comprehensive set of plans for general application to all cases of two-sided limits. However, satisfactory procedures have been found to care for a majority of the applications that will be encountered.

2. TWO-SIDED PLANS FOR USE WHERE THE STANDARD DEVIATION IS KNOWN

One general approach that intuitively seems reasonable for two-sided limits is the simultaneous use of two one-sided tests: one to test for percentage defective above the upper specification limit and one to test for percentage defective below the lower specification limit. Such tests might appropriately be of the same form used for one-sided limits. For example, if only an upper limit U for the measured item characteristic were specified, under a single-limit variables plan the lot would be accepted if for the sample $\bar{x} + k'\sigma \leq U$; if only a lower limit L were specified, the lot would be accepted if $\bar{x} - k'\sigma \geq L$. This suggests that, in cases where an item of product is considered defective if its measured characteristic lies either above an upper bound U or below a lower bound L, the lot be accepted if both of the above single-limit criteria are met.   That is, accept the lot if $\bar{x} + k'\sigma \leq U$ and if $\bar{x} - k'\sigma \geq L$; reject the lot if either one or both criteria are not met.

For many applications the single-limit constants may appropriately be used for two-sided specification limits.   If the expected distribution of item measurements for a product is such that the measurements for defective items in bad lots will be either all above the upper specification limit or all below the lower limit, and if the same AQL classes have been selected for both limits so that the same values for k' will be used in both criteria, then the appropriate value for k' is the one-sided test value for the selected AQL class.   With the expected range of item measurements for each lot so narrow that defectives will all lie on one side of the tolerance range, the sample data for any one lot really need to be evaluated by only one criterion: the criterion for the lower limit if all the defectives will have measurements that are too small, or the criterion for the upper limit if all the defectives will have measurements that are too large.   In actual practice, however, the sample data must be checked against both criteria because it will not always be apparent which of them is appropriate for the lot in question.   However, the data will in effect be evaluated by only one.

The standard deviation for item measurements must be small compared to the specified tolerance, the interval $U - L$.   To ensure this, a minimum range $(U - L)$ must be maintained, and the table below gives this minimum value in terms of σ; for example, if AQL class 1.2 to 2.2 is being used, $U - L$ must be at least 5.6σ, where the constant 5.6 is obtained from this table.

AQL Class, in Percent	Minimum $(U - L)$, in Terms of σ
0.024– 0.035	7.8
0.035– 0.06	7.4
0.06 – 0.12	7.2
0.12 – 0.17	7.0
0.17 – 0.22	6.8
0.22 – 0.32	6.7
0.32 – 0.65	6.6
0.65 – 1.2	6.2
1.2 – 2.2	5.6
2.2 – 3.2	5.4
3.2 – 4.4	5.0
4.4 – 5.3	4.8
5.3 – 6.4	4.5
6.4 – 8.5	4.1
8.5 –11.0	4.0

For values of $(U - L)/\sigma$ slightly lower than the given minimum ones, the specifications cannot be met; that is, even if the distribution of item qualities is centered at the mid-point of the tolerance range (the position which gives the smallest number of defectives), more than the AQL would lie outside the limits. These minimums have also been determined so that in any case virtually all the defectives will lie beyond just one of the limits.

If the same AQL range is used for each of the limits so that the same value for k' is used in each of the criteria, the probability of accepting a lot will be the same for any given percentage defective regardless of whether the defectives are all above the upper limit or all below the lower limit. Hence, under such circumstances it will not matter what proportion of incoming lots have defectives all above U and what proportion have defectives all below L. The over-all effectiveness of the pair of criteria will be the same in any case. Obviously, under these conditions the value of k' (or the values of the corresponding alternative constants k'_a, k'_r, and k'_t) normally used for a one-sided limit is appropriate for use in the pair of criteria for a two-sided test. In this case the realized OC curve will be the same as the single-limit OC curve associated with the selected single-limit plan.

In using this procedure, the criteria for the acceptance of a lot are that both $\bar{x} + k'\sigma \leq U$ and $\bar{x} - k'\sigma \geq L$. All calculations are made in the same manner as for single-limit applications. The use of this procedure when different AQL classes are used for the two limits will be discussed later in this chapter.

3. TWO-SIDED PLANS FOR USE WHERE THE STANDARD DEVIATION IS NOT KNOWN

The use of a pair of plans of the single-limit form is not a satisfactory procedure when the product standard deviation is not known. For some lots the standard deviation may be so large that some of the defectives in the lot lie above the upper limit and some lie below the lower limit. If two one-sided plans are applied in such cases, each plan will test the lot in terms of only part of the defectives it actually contains. A test in terms of the total number of defects will not be applied. This problem is discussed in Chap. 11, Sec. 3.

For this reason an alternative procedure for unknown-sigma applications has been developed. This procedure gives the same probability of acceptance for a lot with a given percentage defective whether the defectives are divided with part lying beyond one limit and part lying beyond the other, or whether they all lie beyond just one limit.

Under this two-limit method all the details of installation and operation are the same as for single-limit specifications except for one step. The calculations to determine the disposal of a lot are different. Instead of an analytical method of applying the acceptance criteria, a graphical test is made.   Sample sizes are the same as for single-limit plans.

The procedure in using this two-limit test is as follows:

(*a*) Prepare a graph to use in evaluating the sample data for each lot. This step is performed prior to the drawing and inspection of samples. Using the selected sample-size letter and AQL class (both of which are selected in the same way as for single-limit products), draw the graph using data obtained from Table P.   This graph will be used to determine the acceptability of each lot.   Its use will give the same operating characteristics as a single-limit plan for the same sample-size letter and AQL class.

Once a graph has been prepared, it may be used for all applications using the same sample size letter and AQL class.

(*b*) Using the specification limits L and U, compute the constant a' where $a' = 2/(U - L)$, and the constant b' where $b' = (L + U)/(L - U)$. Once the constants a' and b' have been computed they may be used for all the lots being tested with this same sample letter and AQL class.

For each lot,

(*c*) Multiply the sample average $\bar{x}$ by a' and add b'.   That is, compute $a'\bar{x} + b'$.   Multiply the sample standard deviation by a'.   That is, compute $a's$.

(*d*) Plot the point $(a'\bar{x} + b', a's)$ on the graph prepared in step (*a*). If the point falls below the curve, accept the lot.   If it falls above the curve, reject the lot.

The procedure above is of a general form in which the same graph may be used for all applications using the same sample-size letter and AQL class.   For applications in which many lots are to be tested, a special graph may be drawn with scales so modified that $\bar{x}$ and s may be plotted directly.   This will eliminate the computations described in (*c*) for each lot.   To draw such a graph, first compute a' and b' by the method shown in (*c*).   Subtract from each abscissa value given in Table P the value b', and then divide the remainder by a'.   For the corresponding ordinate value, take each tabled ordinate value and divide it by a'.

By way of example, an application to purchased parts that have been produced on an automatic screw machine will be outlined.   These parts are to be tested for their diameter.   The specification is that the diameter be between 1.472 inches and 1.488 inches.   For convenience in recording and computing, only the last two digits of measurements will be considered in acceptance inspection.   Thus $L = 72$ and $U = 88$.   Sample-size letter J and AQL class 1.2 to 2.2 has been selected.

Prior to the start of inspection a graph is prepared.   Table P is entered at letter J and at an AQL of 1.2 to 2.2.   Using the points specified, the curve dividing the graph into an acceptance region and a rejection region is drawn. This is shown in Fig. 7.1. This graph is of the general form suitable for all applications for letter J and an AQL of 1.2 to 2.2.

Next, the constants a' and b' are computed. It is found that

$$a' = \frac{2}{(88 - 72)} \text{ or } .125$$

and $$b' = (72 + 88)/(72 - 88) \text{ or } -10.$$

From the first inspection lot a sample of 60 items is drawn and inspected, and the values of $\bar{x}$ and s are found to be 77.3 and 2.1 respectively. Multiplying $\bar{x}$ by a' and adding b' gives -0.34; multiplying

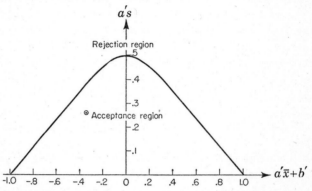

FIG. 7.1. General form of graph for two-sided testing for sample-size letter J and AQL class 1.2 to 2.2 percent.

s by a' gives 0.26. These two computed values are plotted as a point on the graph, -0.34 being used as the abscissa and 0.26 as the ordinate. Since the point plots in the acceptance region, this lot is accepted.

Succeeding lots are tested in the same way and are accepted when the point falls below the curve and rejected when it falls above.

4. THE USE OF DIFFERENT AQL CLASSES FOR EACH OF THE LIMITS

For some products for which a two-sided limit is specified, the acceptance of a defective item whose measurement lies beyond one of the limits may cause much more harm than the acceptance of a defective whose measurement lies beyond the other limit. For example, the tolerance on the diameter of a shaft that must turn in a bearing will probably be so specified, for if the diameter appreciably exceeds the upper limit, it cannot be inserted in the bearing, or if it can be inserted insufficient clearance will be left for adequate lubrication and expansion from temperature changes; on the other hand, if the diameter falls appreciably below the lower limit, the effect will be less serious.   In such a case it would be appropriate to select a relatively small AQL class for the upper limit and a relatively large AQL class for the lower limit.   The graphical procedure described in the previous section cannot be used when different AQL classes are chosen for each limit.   However, a reasonable approach for many applications is the simultaneous use of two single-limit plans.

When the standard deviation is known, the criterion for the acceptance of a lot is that both $\bar{x} + k'_U \sigma \leq U$ and $\bar{x} - k'_L \sigma \geq L$, where k'_U is the constant associated with the AQL class chosen for testing at the upper limit and k'_L is the constant for testing at the lower limit; reject the lot if either one or both of the inequalities are not met.   When the standard deviation is not known, the criterion for acceptance of a lot is that both $\bar{x} + k_U s \leq U$ and $\bar{x} - k_L s \geq L$, where k_U is the constant associated with the AQL class chosen for testing at the upper limit and k_L the constant for testing at the lower limit.

For known-sigma applications and for unknown-sigma applications for which it is known that sigma will generally be so small that all the defectives in a lot will be beyond only one of the limits, information about the operation of a pair of criteria may be obtained by observing the two single-limit OC curves or the AQL and LTPD values.   If for most or all of the lots the defectives will lie above the upper limit, then the OC curve for the single-sided plan used for the upper limit will describe how the pair of plans will discriminate between good and bad lots.   If, on the other hand, for most or all of the lots the defectives will lie below the lower limit, the OC curve for the single-sided plan used for the lower limit will describe how the pair of plans will operate.   If, however, neither of these cases applies, but for part of the submitted lots the defectives have measurements above the upper limit and for the rest the defectives have measurements below the lower limit, the OC curve describing the operation of the pair of plans will lie somewhere between the OC curves for the selected single-limit plans.

For products for which the standard deviation for occasional lots may be so large that the defectives are divided, part lying beyond one limit and part beyond the other, the probability of acceptance will be greater than the probability indicated by either of the OC curves for the selected plans.   Each criterion tests the lot for only part of the defectives, the part beyond the limit to which it is assigned.   If the sample size is small and low AQL classes have been used, the probability of acceptance will be little more than that shown by the higher of the two single-limit curves.   For large sample sizes and large AQL classes the probability of accepting lots with divided defectives will be considerably greater.

CHAPTER 8

ILLUSTRATIVE APPLICATIONS

1. A SINGLE-SAMPLING PLAN AND A SINGLE-SIDED SPECIFICATION LIMIT

A manufacturer purchases from an outside supplier small sheets of rolled metal which he in turn processes further by press operations for ultimate use as one of the parts in the assembly of his own product. To avoid undue difficulties in the purchaser's manufacturing operations and to ensure the production of a satisfactory end product, these sheets of metal should not be too hard or too thin. Accordingly, the receiver's purchase specifications require that the Rockwell (superficial) hardness number (30-N scale) for these sheets be not over a maximum of 68 and that the sheet thickness be not under a minimum of 0.090 inch. These two qualities of the sheets, hardness and thickness, are the only ones which are to be inspected as a basis for acceptance.

The steps followed in installing and operating a variables sampling plan for the acceptance inspection of this product are as follows:

(1) Determining what shall be considered an item of product. These sheets are manufactured individually by the supplier, and the further processing carried out by the receiver is also on a sheet-by-sheet basis. Two of these sheets, after final processing, are used in the assembly of each unit of the receiver's end product. However, the two sheets function independently in this end product and need not match each other in any unique way. The purchase specifications are in terms of individual sheets. In view of these circumstances, the decision is that one sheet of metal will be considered an item of product.

(2) Establishing clearly what makes an item defective. For this product an item is considered defective if (a) its Rockwell (superficial) hardness number (30-N scale) is over 68, (b) it is less than 0.090 inch in thickness, or (c) it fails to meet both these specifications. For this product this step is simple to perform, since the qualities that must be inspected and the limits for each have been definitely established by the receiver's engineering department and appear in the purchase specification.

(3) Selection of an AQL class for each type of defect. After some investigation of the way in which this product is used and a review of the specification limits for each of the properties that are to be meas-

ured, the inspection department finds there are fairly serious consequences if a metal sheet that is much thinner than the specified limit is accepted and used.   Such a sheet is not likely to be detected during the further processing steps that are performed in the receiver's plant and so will be sent on to the assembly department.   When this happens, the assembly in which the sheet is used will not function properly.   Such a failure will be discovered in the final test made on the assembly before it leaves the plant, but the costs of disassembly and then reassembly to replace the defective sheet are considerable.

On the other hand, these rolled sheets are a stock item manufactured by the supplier and must be rolled to a standard nominal size.   Absolute uniformity of thickness cannot be achieved by the supplier's rolling operations, and there would be a considerable increase in manufacturing costs if the average thickness of sheets were to be maintained at a high enough value to ensure virtually no sheets being undersize.   Hence, a compromise must be made.   The receiver's experience with previous shipments of various product from this supplier has shown that approximately 1 percent of the sheets will be under the specified thickness.   However, his knowledge of the kind of processing equipment used by the supplier in the rolling operations leads him to believe that somewhat closer control of sheet thickness is possible.

After consideration of all the above factors, a decision is made to use a plan in the AQL class 0.32 to 0.65 percent defective for this defect.

If a sheet is accepted that is too hard, it may cause some slight difficulties at certain points in the receiver's manufacturing process.   However, the delays occasioned will involve little direct or indirect cost. Such an overhard sheet is likely to enter the assembly department, but it will not appreciably affect the functioning of the assembled product of which it is a part.   Experience with the hardness characteristics of like items purchased in the past indicates that slightly over 1 percent of the items will be defective in this respect.

Since the use of a sheet that is too hard is not serious, the AQL class 0.65 to 1.20 percent defective is selected for use with this defect.

(4) The selection of an inspection level.   Since any sheet with the serious defect of undersize in thickness that may be accepted in an acceptance procedure will eventually be detected and removed in the assembly department, the receiver feels that normal sampling risks can be taken in the acceptance inspection.   Hence inspection level II is selected.   If no opportunity existed to detect and remove these thin sheets prior to shipment of the end product, or if the use of sheets that were too hard would have serious consequences, then a higher inspection level might have been selected.

The four steps described above are performed by an individual at an upper level of inspection management after some consultation with qualified individuals in the engineering and production departments. The remaining steps, as outlined below, are performed or directed by an individual at a lower management level.

(5) Determining how to make up inspection lots. These sheets are shipped from the supplier in boxes, 124 sheets to a box. A ticket is inserted in each box which shows the date on which they were produced and the supplier's serial number for the machine which rolled the sheets. To meet the general sampling inspection requirement that inspection lots be made up of items produced under like conditions, an attempt is to be made to form lots by combining only boxes of sheets produced by the same machine and by combining, as far as this is possible, only sheets produced by this machine during the same day. In consideration of the number of different rolling machines that may be used by the supplier to produce this product, the usual quantity produced per day per machine, and the rate of shipment to the receiver, the combination of three boxes to form an inspection lot of 372 sheets seems most appropriate. If inspection lots of fewer items were to be formed, acceptance inspection costs would be appreciably increased with little gain in quality assurance; if lots with a greater number of items were to be formed, this would often require the grouping of items produced by different machines or produced during different days and thus reduce the effectiveness of sampling inspection.

(6) Determining the sample-size letter. This step is carried out in a routine manner by reference to Table A, Sample-size Letter, by Inspection Level and Size of Inspection Lot. An inspection lot of 372 items falls in the 300- to 500-item lot-size range as shown on the sixth line of the table. Reading across the table on this line to the column for inspection level II shows that sample-size letter G is the appropriate one to use.

(7) The selection of the type of sampling plan to be used. For this application, the drawing of sample items at random from an inspection lot is a relatively difficult step. On the other hand, the measurements of item characteristics are relatively easy to take, both for hardness and for thickness. Hence, a single-sampling form of plan seems most appropriate. No evidence is available to show that the standard deviation of item values for either of the properties will remain more or less fixed, so a general plan for use when the standard deviation is not known must be used.

(8) The selection of a specific sampling plan for each type of defect. For this step, Table E, which lists both the single-sampling and the double-sampling plans together with their operating characteristic curves,

will be used. The plans in this table are classified by sample-size letter and by AQL class. The sixth page of this table contains the plans for sample-size letter G, the letter selected for this application.

From this page, the following information is obtained:

(*a*) The sample size for letter G which is 25 items.

(*b*) The factor k for use in the acceptance criterion for sample data on sheet thickness. A value for k of 1.993 is found on the line for AQL class 0.32 to 0.65, the class chosen for this item characteristic.

(*c*) The factor k for use in the acceptance criterion for sample data on hardness. A value for k of 1.756 is found on the line for AQL class 0.65 to 1.20, the class chosen for this item characteristic.

This example will illustrate the use of the standard form of the acceptance criterion. For some of the optional forms described in the Appendix, values for k_w, k_x, k_y, and k_z would be obtained from Table F for each item quality being considered instead of values for k.

(9) *The formation of inspection lots.* As shipments of this material are received, boxes are grouped into inspection lots, three boxes to a lot in accordance with the procedure determined in step (5). For acceptance inspection purposes, each lot is marked with a serial number which will be used for identification of the lot in each of the succeeding steps that will be performed.

(10) *The drawing of samples from the inspection lots.* The inspector is instructed to draw 8 sheets from each of two of the boxes making up an inspection lot and 9 sheets from the third box, giving a total of 25 items, the specified sample size. He is also instructed to take sheets at random throughout each box, starting near or at the top and working down to the bottom. This step is performed in turn for each of the inspection lots formed from each shipment.

(11) *Inspection of the items making up each of the samples.* Measurements are taken for the thickness and the hardness for each item in each of the samples. The measurements for the items in a typical sample are given in Table 8.1.

(12) *Making computations required to determine the proper disposal of each lot.* The mean $\bar{x}$ and the standard deviation s are calculated for each set of measurements, those for hardness and those for thickness. The values of $\bar{x}$ and s are then used in the standard form of the acceptance criteria to determine the disposal of each lot. Details of the method and for making these calculations are given in the Appendix.

For the lot whose measurements for sample items are given in Table 8.1, the mean for the thickness readings $\bar{x}$ is calculated to be 0.1085 inch; the standard deviation s is 0.006462. Since the limit for sheet thickness is a lower limit L, the acceptance criterion is

$$\bar{x} - ks \geq L \tag{5}$$

where
$$L = 0.090$$

Inserting the appropriate values in the formula gives

$$0.1085 - (1.993)(0.006462) = 0.09562$$

Since $\bar{x} - ks$ is greater than the limit 0.090, the lot is acceptable in so far as sheet thickness is concerned.

TABLE 8.1.   MEASUREMENTS FOR A SAMPLE DRAWN FROM LOT No. 342

Item	Thickness, in inches	Rockwell hardness number
1	0.103	64
2	0.101	57
3	0.107	65
4	0.108	59
5	0.112	59
6	0.115	59
7	0.100	60
8	0.112	62
9	0.113	66
10	0.106	65
11	0.098	59
12	0.113	61
13	0.099	60
14	0.111	61
15	0.101	61
16	0.118	60
17	0.111	56
18	0.108	57
19	0.113	62
20	0.113	60
21	0.114	61
22	0.099	57
23	0.113	61
24	0.121	62
25	0.103	64

For the Rockwell hardness readings for this sample, the mean $\bar{x}$ is found to be 60.7 and the standard deviation s is found to be 2.65. Since the hardness limit is an upper limit U, the criterion for acceptance is that

$$\bar{x} + ks \leq U \qquad (4)$$

where
$$U = 68$$

Inserting the appropriate values in the formula gives

$$60.7 + (1.756)(2.65) = 65.4$$

Since $\bar{x} + ks$ is less than the limit 68, the lot is acceptable for this defect.

Inasmuch as the data from the sample meets the acceptance criterion for each of the defects, the lot is accepted. If it had failed to meet either test, the lot would have been rejected.

(13) Computation of the process average. Steps (10) to (12) are repeated for each inspection lot with the result that most of the lots are accepted, only an occasional one being rejected. Twenty lots have been inspected, and it now seems advisable to compute the process average for each defect to see whether or not the two plans now being used are appropriate for future shipments.

TABLE 8.2.   VALUES OF MEANS AND STANDARD DEVIATIONS FOR TWENTY SAMPLES

Sample	Thickness, in inches		Hardness	
	$\bar{x}$	s	$\bar{x}$	s
1	0.1085	0.006462	60.7	2.65
2	0.1063	0.006009	60.6	2.54
3	0.1051	0.006719	61.0	3.08
4	0.1031	0.006307	60.8	2.32
5	0.1060	0.006135	60.5	2.95
6	0.1054	0.006575	61.5	2.84
7	0.1048	0.005503	61.5	2.22
8	0.1043	0.003727	60.4	3.03
9	0.1048	0.006628	61.3	3.35
10	0.1027	0.005821	62.1	3.80
11	0.1047	0.006507	61.4	2.50
12	0.1030	0.005364	60.9	2.85
13	0.1047	0.005727	60.9	2.77
14	0.1068	0.005973	60.8	2.74
15	0.1044	0.006861	61.1	3.05
16	0.1036	0.005025	61.6	2.73
17	0.1061	0.008175	61.5	3.36
18	0.1029	0.006676	60.9	3.63
19	0.1034	0.005816	60.9	2.43
20	0.1042	0.006992	62.1	2.70

Accordingly, data from the 20 inspection lots submitted to the plans is collected. The results of the 20 samples from these 20 lots are given in Table 8.2.

Since the sample size n is the same from lot to lot, the grand lot mean $\bar{\bar{x}}$ is found by the formula

$$\bar{\bar{x}} = \frac{n}{N} \sum \bar{x} \tag{19}$$

and the grand lot standard deviation $\bar{\bar{s}}$ is found by the formula

$$\bar{\bar{s}} = \sqrt{\frac{(n-1)\Sigma s^2 + n\Sigma\bar{x}^2 - (n^2/N)(\Sigma\bar{x})^2}{N-1}} \tag{20}$$

For sheet thickness, $\bar{\bar{x}}$ is found to be 0.1047 and $\bar{\bar{s}}$ is found to be 0.006262. For hardness readings, $\bar{\bar{x}}$ is found to be 61.1 and $\bar{\bar{s}}$ is found to be 2.89.

Values for $\bar{k}$ are then calculated for each inspected characteristic using the formulas

$$\bar{k} = \frac{U - \bar{\bar{x}}}{\bar{\bar{s}}} \tag{23}$$

and

$$\bar{k} = \frac{\bar{\bar{x}} - L}{\bar{\bar{s}}} \tag{24}$$

For sheet thickness

$$\bar{k} = \frac{0.1047 - 0.090}{0.006262} = 2.35$$

and for hardness

$$\bar{k} = \frac{68 - 61.1}{2.89} = 2.39$$

These values for $\bar{k}$ are then taken, one at a time, to Chart G, Estimated Process Average as a Function of $\bar{k}$. From this table, the process average or estimate of the percent defective for these 20 lots for each type of defect is found. The estimate for sheets under minimum thickness is 0.94 percent and for sheets over maximum hardness is 0.84 percent. Note that the percentage of sheets too thin is larger than the AQL class of 0.32 to 0.65 percent which was selected for this application and that the percentage of sheets too hard is within the selected AQL class of 0.65 to 1.20 percent defective.

(14) Determining whether tightened or reduced inspection should be applied. Inspection of the information obtained by the previous step shows that for the Rockwell hardness readings the process average falls within the bounds of the selected AQL class. Since the bounds of the AQL classes are narrower than the corresponding process average limits, it is clear that normal inspection should be maintained for this charac-

teristic.   However, the percentage of sheets under the allowable minimum for thickness is greater than the upper bound of the AQL class selected for this defect.   A reference must be made to Table H, Upper and Lower Limits on Process Average, to determine whether or not tightened inspection is indicated.   This table is entered on the first line inasmuch as the process average is based on 500 sample items (20 samples of 25 items each).   Following across the table on this line to the 0.32 to 0.65 AQL column, it is found that the calculated value 0.94 for the process average falls below the upper limit 1.05.   This indicates that the presented quality has not differed significantly from the selected AQL class range.   Hence, normal inspection should be maintained for both characteristics.

2. A DOUBLE-SAMPLING PLAN AND A SINGLE-SIDED SPECIFICATION LIMIT

A manufacturer purchases from another concern several sizes of stud bolts made from a special alloy steel for use in assembling his own product. One section of the purchase specification requires a minimum tensile strength of 125,000 pounds per square inch.   Sample bolts from submitted lots of product are to be inspected for this quality characteristic, and the inspection results used as a basis for acceptance or rejection of each lot.

The steps followed in installing and operating a variables sampling plan for the acceptance inspection of this product are as follows:

(1) Determining what shall be considered an item product.   In the manufacturing of these stud bolts, part of the processing is on a bolt-by-bolt basis and the rest is by very large batches.   The bolts are used in the manufacturer's product in small groups.   However, no unique match is required among the bolts in a group.   Hence, one bolt is considered an item of product.

(2) Establishing clearly what makes an item defective.   The only test to be made for the acceptance inspection procedure is the one for tensile strength.   An item is to be considered defective if its tensile strength is less than 125,000 pounds per square inch.   Dimensional tolerances are also specified for these bolts, but as no defectives because of dimensions are expected, the acceptance procedure will not consider these properties.

(3) The selection of an AQL class.   It is quite important that these bolts be of adequate strength.   The receiver's experience with like products leads him to believe that the supplier can keep the percentage of items failing to meet the specification limit well below $\frac{1}{4}$ of 1 percent. In view of these considerations a decision is made to use a plan in the 0.17 to 0.22 AQL class.

(4) The selection of an inspection level.   It is quite desirable that the risk of accepting inspection lots whose percent defective is higher than the AQL range be minimized.   This consideration would call for the use of inspection level III and its relatively large sample size.   On the other hand the inspection of an item takes a large amount of time, and the necessary inspection facilities are limited.   After considering in detail each of these determinants, a decision is made to compromise and use inspection level II.

(5) Determining how to make up inspection lots.   These bolts are shipped from the supplier in boxes of 300 bolts to the box.   Each box is marked to show the supplier's serial number for the machine which produced the bolts and their date of production.   As the production rate per machine is low, it seems that fairly homogeneous inspection lots can be formed by considering each box as an inspection lot.   If this is done, product produced on different days and by different machines will not be mixed.

(6) Determining the sample-size letter.   This step is carried out by reference to Table A.   An inspection-lot size of 300 items is found to fall on the border line between two adjacent lot-size ranges.   A decision is arbitrarily made to use the 200 to 300 lot-size range.   For this range and for inspection level II, the use of sample-size letter F is indicated by Table A.

(7) The selection of the type of sampling plan to be used.   The testing of an item is relatively costly in inspection time, and the item is destroyed by the test.   Hence it is desirable to keep sample sizes as small as possible.   Also, samples can readily be drawn from the inspection lot as they are needed.   For these reasons a decision is made to use a double-sampling plan.

(8) The selection of a specific sampling plan.   For this step, Table E is used.   The fifth page of this table contains plans for sample-size letter F.   From this page the following information is obtained:

(a) The first and second sample sizes, which are 8 items and 16 items, respectively.

(b) The factors for use in the double-sampling criteria.   The value for k_a, the factor for the first-sample acceptance criterion, is 3.041; k_r, the factor for the first-sample rejection criterion, is 1.344; k_t, the factor for the acceptance criterion for combined samples, is 2.245.

(9) The drawing of first samples from inspection lots.   The inspector is instructed to draw at random from each shipping box (one box constituting an inspection lot) a first sample of eight bolts.

(10) Inspection of the items making up each of the first samples.   Strength tests are made, and the actual readings in pounds for the maxi-

mum test load for each bolt (converted to ultimate strength in pounds per square inch of cross-sectional area) are recorded. The values for items in a typical sample are given in Table 8.3.

(11) Application of the acceptance criterion for first samples. In order to simplify the computations, the first digit, which will always be 1, and the last two digits, which will always be 00 (since the values are measured to the nearest 500 pounds), are omitted. The transformed values are shown in the third column of Table 8.3. The corresponding transformation of the specified lower limit, 125,000, yields an L of 250.

For the lot whose first-sample measurements are shown in Table 8.3,

TABLE 8.3.   MEASUREMENTS FOR A FIRST AND A SECOND SAMPLE DRAWN FROM LOT NO. 11

Item	Ultimate strength, in pounds per square inch	Transformed readings
First sample		
1	129,500	295
2	131,000	310
3	128,500	285
4	126,500	265
5	130,000	300
6	130,500	305
7	127,500	275
8	129,000	290
Second sample		
9	129,500	295
10	131,000	310
11	129,500	295
12	128,000	280
13	129,000	290
14	127,000	270
15	132,500	325
16	130,500	305
17	129,000	290
18	130,000	300
19	133,000	330
20	129,000	290
21	131,500	315
22	130,000	300
23	132,000	320
24	128,500	285

the first-sample mean $\bar{x}_1$ is found to be 290.6 and the first-sample standard deviation s_1 is found to be 15.22. Substituting these values into the first-sample acceptance criterion

$$\bar{x}_1 - k_a s_1 \geq L \tag{9}$$

gives $\qquad 290.6 - (3.041)(15.22) = 244$

Since $\bar{x}_1 - k_a s_1$ is not greater than L, which is 250, this lot cannot be accepted on the basis of the data from the first sample.

(12) Application of the rejection criterion for first samples. For this sample, substituting the values for $\bar{x}_1$ and s_1 into the first-sample rejection criterion

$$\bar{x}_1 - k_r s_1 \leq L \tag{11}$$

gives $\qquad 290.6 - (1.344)(15.22) = 270$

Since $\bar{x}_1 - k_r s_1$ is not less than 250, this lot is not rejected on the basis of information from the first sample.

(13) The drawing of second samples and inspection of second-sample items. If neither acceptance nor rejection is indicated for a lot by the first-sample criteria, a second sample is drawn and the items inspected. For the illustration lot, the second-sample measurements are in Table 8.3.

(14) Application of the acceptance criterion for combined samples. Where second samples must be taken, measurements for the first and second samples are combined and the mean $\bar{x}_t$ and the standard deviation s_t for the combined sample calculated. These values are then used in the combined-sample acceptance criterion to determine the final disposal of the lot.

For the lot whose sample measurements are shown in Table 8.3, the combined-sample mean $\bar{x}_t$ is 296.9 and the combined-sample standard deviation s_t is 16.47. Substituting these values into the combined-sample acceptance criterion

$$\bar{x}_t - k_t s_t \geq L \tag{15}$$

gives $\qquad 296.9 - (2.245)(16.47) = 260$

Since $\bar{x}_t - k_t s_t$ is greater than L, which is 250, the lot is judged acceptable.

(15) Computation of the process average and determining whether tightened or reduced inspection should be applied. Steps (9) to (14) are applied as needed to each inspection lot. After 38 lots or so are inspected (to yield a total of at least three hundred items), a process average is calculated to help in determining whether normal inspection may be continued or reduced or tightened inspection will be more appropriate. This procedure is carried out in the same manner as under single sampling. The one point of difference is that only measurements from first samples are used in computing the process average.

CHAPTER 9

THE USE OF CONTROL CHARTS IN SAMPLING INSPECTION

1. MEANING OF CONTROL

The differences in dimensions, hardness, and other properties of a product from one item to the next are produced by a great number of causes acting simultaneously. Most of these differences arise because raw materials cannot be produced or be found that are entirely uniform in all their properties; because machines vibrate, wear, and for other reasons do not function in a perfectly uniform manner; and because of the natural variations of the workman in performing his part in production processes.

In statistical techniques for quality control, it is convenient to think of these variation-producing causes as being divided into two distinct categories. The first category includes causes, usually of minor importance, that are impossible or uneconomical to eliminate and hence can be considered inherent in the processes used in producing the product. This inherent system of causes is present during the production of each item. However, the extent of the effect of each one of these causes making up the system varies, usually in a chance manner. Their combined effect during the production of one item will not be the same as their combined effect during the production of the next. However, if these variation-producing causes were the only ones present over a period of production, the end result would be the manufacture of lots of product whose measured item characteristics would form stable frequency distributions around their averages—distributions that would usually be normal.

The other category of variation-producing causes includes, in effect, those having a relatively great influence on the variation of item properties and which suddenly enter or increase rapidly in effectiveness to remain for a relatively long time in the production process. These causes have been named "assignable" causes. The entrance of an assignable cause affects to a noticeable degree the distribution of measurements as formerly produced by the inherent system of minor causes; it may raise or lower the average around which the minor causes distribute individual measurements, or it may increase or may decrease the dispersion of the measurements. Sometimes such a cause may affect both the average and the dispersion.

Actually, whether a cause is an assignable one or is one that may be considered part of the system of chance causes inherent in the process is a relative matter in many cases. The classification of a cause may depend primarily on how noticeable its effect is as compared with other causes present. Also, its classification may depend to some extent on how frequently it appears and the length of time it remains in the process.

When a production process is operating with only its inherent system of minor and chance-acting, variation-producing causes present, the process is said to be "in control." When an assignable cause enters, the process is then considered to have gone "out of control." The control chart is a statistical tool which is receiving increasing use to determine whether or not control is present and, for processes in which some degree of control has been achieved, to indicate the presence of an assignable cause if one should enter.

Control charts for measurements indicate control or lack of control by means of statistically determined limits for sample data. These limits show a range of normal variation for the averages and for the dispersions of measurements for samples of relatively few items if taken from the process when it is in control. The maximum deviations from the expected values for data from any one subgroup or sample, as indicated by the limits, take into account the expected range of errors arising from sampling. As long as values for the average and dispersion of measurements from sample to sample fall between their respective limits, one can assume that the process is in control. A value for sample data that falls beyond one of the limits indicates a marked change in the process—items are being produced about a different average or with a different pattern of dispersion; that is, an assignable cause has thrown the process out of control.

This brief and elementary discussion of control is intended to serve only as an introduction and background for the rest of this chapter. The reader who is not familiar with the control chart technique should consult one or more of the excellent books now available on this subject for complete details of the theory and practice.†

2. THE CONTROL CHART IN ACCEPTANCE INSPECTION

The control chart procedure and the sampling inspection procedure for acceptance both use data from a relatively small sample to evaluate the population of items from which the sample was drawn. However, they

† See Eugene L. Grant, "Statistical Quality Control," McGraw-Hill Book Company, Inc., New York, 1946; American War Standard Z1.3—1942, "Control Chart Method for Controlling Quality during Production," American Standards Association, New York, 1942.

ordinarily have entirely different objectives.   In acceptance inspection, information is obtained from the sample to decide solely whether or not the lot of completed product from which it was taken is good enough to accept under criteria that have been more or less arbitrarily established in accord with a desired quality.   Sample data for the control chart, on the other hand, is used to judge the product in various stages of its production in terms of the quality that the operations themselves have shown they can produce.   The chart is ordinarily used only for locating assignable causes of variation and in making adjustments to certain machines and equipment, so that a more satisfactory product will be produced in the future.   Little or no direct use is made of the chart or the sample data in deciding on the acceptability of particular lots of product.

The control chart can, however, play a useful part in acceptance inspection, and some use has been made of the technique in this connection. It seems particularly appropriate to consider its use when acceptance inspection is on a variables basis, since data is available to maintain the most efficient form of control charts—those for the average and the dispersion of item measurements.   Under attribute acceptance inspection, only the relatively inefficient charts in terms of percent defective or the number of defectives can be used without making additional inspections. Under these variables acceptance plans, the calculated values for the sample mean and the sample standard deviation can be used directly for plotting on control charts, no further inspections or calculations being needed.

The chief value of the control chart as a tool in acceptance inspection will, in most cases, be the general picture it gives of the quality history of the products to which it has been applied.   In the control chart analysis, the data from a number of lots is combined in a way that gives a much more revealing description of submitted quality than data from each lot standing alone.   From this supplemental information about product that has been received, one may obtain guidance in the acceptance inspection of product that will be submitted in the future.

One possible form of guidance from the control chart is its use in selecting an inspection level and in deciding whether or not to go on tightened or on reduced inspection.   For example, if a product from a supplier has been in control for some time, inspection level I might be used instead of inspection level II, the one normally selected.   This will reduce the sample size, which, in turn, will reduce inspection costs.   Less protection will be given by the lot-by-lot acceptance procedure, but since fewer unacceptable lots are likely to be received from processes that have been in control, this change can safely be made.   If, on the other hand, control charts show lack of control for some product, operation of acceptance inspection under inspection level II, or perhaps under inspection level III, may be necessary to give adequate protection against the unacceptable lots that can be expected. Although complete and detailed rules cannot be laid down for this use of the control chart, evidence of control or of lack of control should be of considerable help to those supervising acceptance inspection when choosing an inspection level—a task that at best cannot be carried out with any degree of exactness. When some one product is being submitted by several suppliers, evidence from control charts should be of particular assistance in justifying the use of a different inspection level for one supplier than for another, particularly if there is little difference in their process averages.

Control charts may to some extent be used in a like manner as a guide to the selection of an acceptable quality level. However, from a theoretical point of view, the presence of control or the lack of control should be reflected in the choice of an inspection level. If we assume that the primary object of acceptance inspection is to separate bad lots from those which are good, the sharp discrimination given by the larger sample sizes called for by a higher inspection level is particularly needed when a product is from an out-of-control process. On the other hand, if one wishes to use acceptance inspection also to discriminate against or to apply pressure to the supplier of product whose processes are not so well controlled, some allowance might be made when choosing the AQL. The choice of a lower AQL figure than one might otherwise use will increase rejections and thus may induce him to bring his processes under control. Another advantage, from the receiver's standpoint, of lowering the AQL rather than raising the inspection level under such circumstances is that acceptance inspection costs will not be increased owing to larger sample sizes. The extra costs, at least for the time being, for securing the extra protection needed by the receiver of goods from out-of-control processes fall where they rightly should be—on the supplier. The receiver should remember, however, that it is possible in some cases that nothing can be done to bring the supplier's operations into control or that no attempts on the part of the supplier to do so will be made. Then the extra costs of getting the needed protection in this way may eventually enter the selling price of the article.

Where a close and cooperative relationship exists between the supplier and the receiver, control charts or information from charts may be exchanged. Charts properly prepared from acceptance inspection data, if sent to the supplier, can sometimes be of considerable assistance to him in process improvement, particularly if he has not been plotting charts on his operations himself. Likewise, if the supplier who does use control charts submits charts along with his product, they may be of great help to the receiver in planning acceptance inspection.

Control charts plotted from acceptance inspection data can assist the receiver in another way. Suppose, for example, that the chart history for a product shows that close control is being maintained by the producer. This means, in effect, that there will be little difference in the frequency distribution of item properties from one inspection lot to the next, particularly if the lots are large. When there is little difference in quality from one lot to the next, sampling inspection will be of little help, as explained in Chap. 3. Some lots will be accepted and some will be rejected, the decision for any particular lot depending mainly on how chance has influenced the drawing of the sample. Suppose also that the average level about which measurements are controlled is such that the percent defective is at or somewhat above the AQL for the sampling plan in use. Under such circumstances, an appreciable number of inspection lots will probably be rejected. In the absence of any knowledge that control exists, the receiver will very likely feel that sampling inspection is doing an effective job in weeding out many of the defective items. Actually, of course, under our assumption of the process being in control, the lots being accepted are of about the same quality as those being submitted or as those being rejected. Thus, with no information available about the degree of control for a product, it may in some cases be difficult to know whether rejections are being made because some lots are markedly worse than others or whether there is little difference between lots and the rejections occur primarily because by chance an occasional sample represents its lot to be worse than the others. Thus, with no knowledge of control, there may be considerable waste of time in ineffective acceptance sampling inspection, in some cases.

If, however, the controlled item characteristics are between values such that the percent defective in lots will fall at or below the selected AQL, the consequences are of a different nature. All, or practically all, of the inspection lots will meet the acceptance criteria and will be accepted. The desired protection is assured, and there will be no useless rejection of inspection lots. Here again, knowledge of the state of control can be of use. If control at a level which produces few items outside specification limits has been shown for some time, the sample size for variables acceptance inspection can, as mentioned before, be reduced by choosing a lower inspection level, or it may be possible to discontinue acceptance sampling inspection and rely entirely on control charts, accepting all lots as long as control continues to be shown. If this last alternative is followed, it will be possible to use the customary control chart sample of four or five items to maintain the charts and thus keep acceptance inspection costs at a minimum. Another advantage of maintaining control charts when submitted quality is running considerably better than the AQL is that, if control should be lost, this may be detected fairly promptly, perhaps before the process has become bad enough to produce some lots that should be rejected. The inspection level can be raised, or other appropriate steps taken at once to give the necessary protection until a state of control at a satisfactory level is again achieved. In any event, when a product is good enough so that all lots are being accepted by a sampling inspection plan, the charts will give the worthwhile knowledge that the product is controlled (and, if so, at what level) or that it is not controlled but happens to be good enough so all lots do meet the sampling inspection acceptance criterion.

In the above discussion of the uses of the control chart as an adjunct to sampling inspection, there may seem to be some implication that, unless control charts had been plotted, one would know nothing about how well quality had been controlled. This is not true, of course. An informal analysis can be made of acceptance inspection results, and in a general way, the extent of variation from lot to lot noted. Also, rejected lots can be identified, and the information found in sampling inspection noted and sent to the producer to assist in identifying assignable causes of variations. A great deal more can be learned, however, when sample data is observed in relation to the variations possible because of chance, as is done when values are plotted and compared with the limit lines on control charts.

In the use of control charts in acceptance inspection, a few precautions should be observed. The first is that no attempt should be made to make the acceptance or rejection of a particular inspection lot depend on whether or not the point representing it on the chart falls between the control limits. The control limits are set by the machines and operations used in producing the product and may bear no direct relation to the receiver's acceptance standards, which are usually set in terms of the quality he can accept. Under the use of both control charts and a variables sampling inspection plan, it may happen, as mentioned before, that some product may show lack of control but that the general run of quality is so much better than the AQL that all lots will be acceptable. A clear distinction must be kept in mind between the function of the limit lines on the control chart and the function of the acceptance criterion of a variables inspection plan.

A second point is that, when goods are received from a supplier intermittently with long periods between each shipment, much less reliance can be placed on control chart information. When charts are plotted by the receiver from measurements on finished product he has received, their chief use is in planning the inspection of future shipments, their usefulness being based on the assumption that the quality history of the product which has been produced has some validity in predicting the quality of product that will be produced in the future. If a long period has elapsed since the last shipment, there is a good possibility of significant changes in the producer's processes during that time, so that charts kept on past shipments will not be very reliable indicators of what quality can be expected in the shipments currently being received.

Under the use of single-sampling acceptance plans, the sample as a whole is considered a control chart subgroup and the data from it used for charting in the customary way. Under double sampling, data from the first sample only is used, so that subgroups will be kept at a constant size. Samples should be inspected and points plotted on the charts as nearly as possible in the order of their production, although this rule may be difficult to carry out at times. Charts lose a great deal of their value as a guide to action when the order of production is lost.

3. CONTROL LIMITS FOR THE MEANS OF SAMPLES

The most useful type of control chart for the general run of industrial applications is the chart for sample means or averages. It is highly useful because, first, assignable causes that throw a manufacturing process out of control will most likely affect the average measurement for the item characteristic. The usual assignable causes in machine operations frequently have little effect, and sometimes no effect, on the dispersion of measurements. For example, tool wear, the slippage of adjustments, or improper machine settings affect only the average of measurements from most operations. Not only is the average of item measurements the property that is most likely to change, but also it is usually possible for this characteristic to stray a relatively great distance from the desired value. The possible variation in dispersion of measurements is usually more restricted, at least in machine operations. Hence, the average is the statistic that should be watched most closely unless there is evidence that some other measure will be more appropriate for the particular product at hand. The chart for averages is often the only one plotted for an item characteristic, particularly when through use of control charts in the past one finds that the dispersion of items is fairly well controlled.

Another advantage of the average as a measure of control is that statistically it is quite reliable. Averages of samples from a normal universe form a normal distribution of their own, clustering relatively close about the universe average. Furthermore, for the universe that is badly skewed or in other ways far from normal, the averages of samples tend to approximate a normal distribution as the number of items in the sample increases.   For the sample sizes used in these variables plans, the approach will be quite close for almost any industrial product that will be encountered.   Still another advantage is that for some products it is most important that the average of measurements remain unchanged, the dispersion of measurements from item to item being relatively less important.   Under these circumstances, the average chart should obviously receive first consideration.

As previously mentioned, the averages for samples will tend to cluster around the true average for the universe, or grand lot, from which they came.   This true value μ will not be known, but an estimate of it can be obtained by taking the average of the averages from a number of inspection lots.   This estimate $\bar{\bar{x}}$ is used to analyze the past data from which it is calculated.   If the analysis shows a state of control during the production of these lots, this value $\bar{\bar{x}}$ can be taken as an estimate of the true process or grand lot average μ and used in drawing the center line on the chart for checking future production for control.   Obviously, the more items used in obtaining $\bar{\bar{x}}$, the more accurate it will be.   Common control chart practice is to use at least twenty subgroups of four or five items. Since the averages obtained from the operation of these variables plans are from samples considerably larger than those generally used for control charts, the number of subgroups used in getting this estimate may be somewhat less.

Since any one sample is not likely truly to represent the population from which it is drawn, its average will deviate somewhat from the true average of the population μ.   The control lines on the chart for averages are placed on each side of the line representing the estimate of the true average at a distance great enough to care for these deviations.

The extent of deviations of sample averages due to sampling error will depend on two things.   It will depend first of all on the number of items in the samples.   The larger the sample size n, the more closely values for $\bar{x}$ will cluster around μ, the true average, since larger samples are apt to represent the universe from which they are drawn more closely.

The second determinant of the spread of the distribution of sample averages is the dispersion, or spread of measurements for items in the population; the larger the dispersion of the item values, the larger the variations in the sample mean.

The standard deviation $\sigma_{\bar{x}}$ of the distribution of sample averages is given by the equation

$$\sigma_{\bar{x}} = \frac{\sigma}{\sqrt{n}} \tag{34}$$

The 3-sigma control limits customarily used will thus be placed at a distance of

$$3 \frac{\sigma}{\sqrt{n}}$$

from the central line as it is drawn at the value for $\bar{x}$ on the chart.   If σ is estimated from an average sample standard deviation $\bar{s}$ as discussed in Sec. 4 below, the limits will be placed at a distance of

$$\frac{3\bar{s}}{\sqrt{\dfrac{2}{n-1}} \dfrac{[(n-2)/2]!}{[(n-3)/2]!} \sqrt{n}}$$

from the central line.   Values for the constants A and $\hat{A}_1$,† where

$$A = \frac{3}{\sqrt{n}} \tag{35}$$

and

$$\hat{A}_1 = \frac{3}{\sqrt{\dfrac{2}{n-1}} \dfrac{[(n-2)/2]!}{[(n-3/2)]!} \sqrt{n}} \tag{36}$$

have been calculated and are listed in Table J.   Values will be found here for all sample sizes arising from these variables plans, values for each single-sample size and for each first sample size for the double-sampling plans.   (As pointed out before, data from only the first sample should be used when double-sampling plans are in operation, since for many lots a second sample is not taken.)

Limit lines can thus be obtained by the expression

$$\bar{x} \pm \hat{A}_1 \bar{s} \tag{37}$$

for initial use on the chart in analyzing past inspection data for control, where $\bar{s}$ is the mean of the standard deviations of the samples from lots over the past period being considered.   The expression

$$\bar{x} \pm A\sigma \tag{38}$$

is used after a standard value for the standard deviation of the population has been adopted.   Procedures for calculating $\bar{s}$ will be outlined in the next section.

† The constants $\hat{c}_2$, $\hat{A}_1$, $\hat{B}_1$, $\hat{B}_2$, $\hat{B}_3$, and $\hat{B}_4$ differ from the c_2, A_1, B_1, B_2, B_3, and B_4 commonly used in control chart technique because the sample standard deviation is computed with $n-1$ in the denominator instead of n.   The circumflex ($\wedge$) is used to indicate this difference.   The constants thus marked have a use similar to those in common practice, and the control charts drawn with either set of constants will be identical.

4. CONTROL LIMITS FOR THE STANDARD DEVIATIONS OF SAMPLES

Often it is desirable to know not only how well the average of measurements is being controlled but also the degree of control over the dispersion of measurements about this average. In industrial quality control charts the usual measure of dispersion of measurements within the subgroup or sample is the range R. This measure has been used because it is easy to calculate and because it is easily understood by persons at all levels in industry. However, if control charts are plotted with data from variables acceptance inspection, a more precise and statistically more efficient measure of dispersion, the standard deviation is readily available. Hence, charts for the sample standard deviation are recommended instead of the usual range charts. In fact, direct use of all the acceptance inspection data will require the use of s most of the time; the range is a suitable measure only when the subgroup size is quite small, say less than twelve items. Beyond this figure the range rapidly loses its reliability. For many products, sample sizes under these variables plans will be considerably greater than twelve.

Customary control chart practice is to use the arithmetic average of the sample standard deviation $\bar{s}$ as the center line of the control chart, and this procedure is recommended here. Another method would be to base the center line on $\bar{s}$, the pooled standard deviation of all the observations taken to date. However, the use of $\bar{s}$ assumes implicitly that all the samples are taken from populations with the same mean quality; clearly this assumption may not be valid in many cases in which we want to draw control charts for the standard deviation.

However, one important departure from standard practice should be noted: Most books and pamphlets on quality control recommend that the sample standard deviation be computed from the formula

$$s = \sqrt{\frac{\Sigma(x - \bar{x})^2}{n}} \tag{39}$$

but in this book we have followed the method commonly used in statistics books and have defined the sample standard deviation as

$$s = \sqrt{\frac{\Sigma(x - \bar{x})^2}{n - 1}} \tag{2}$$

This value $\bar{s}$, assuming control has been shown, cannot be used directly as an estimate for the true standard deviation σ for the population from which the samples were drawn. The standard deviations for samples tend, on the average, to be a little less than the universe standard deviation. The amount of this bias depends on the sample size and is expressed by a factor conventionally represented by $\hat{c}_2$.   If the universe is approximately normal, the universe standard deviation σ can be found by the formula

$$\sigma = \frac{\bar{s}}{\hat{c}_2} \qquad (40)$$

The value for $\hat{c}_2$ for any sample size can be found by the formula

$$\hat{c}_2 = \sqrt{\frac{2}{n-1}} \frac{[(n-2)/2]!}{[(n-3)/2]!} \qquad (41)$$

Values for $\hat{c}_2$ have been calculated for each value of n arising from these variables plans and are listed in Table J.

The value for $\bar{s}$, the average of sample standard deviations, or the value for $\hat{c}_2\sigma$ must be used for the center line on the sigma control chart.   The estimate of the population standard deviation σ is calculated so that limit lines may be located both on these charts and on the charts for averages.

The extent to which sample standard deviations will be distributed about the average of sample standard deviations $\bar{s}$ depends, as for sample averages, on the sample size and on the dispersion of item measurements within the population from which the samples have been drawn.   The possible amount of dispersion of sample standard deviations decreases as the sample size increases.   Also, the smaller the dispersion of item measurements in the population, the smaller will be the possible range of values for the sample standard deviation.   For a normally distributed universe, the standard deviation for the distribution of sample standard deviations is given by the formula

$$\sigma_s = \frac{\sigma}{\sqrt{2n}} \qquad (42)$$

Three-sigma control limits for the standard deviations of samples will thus be placed on each side of the central line at a distance $3\sigma/\sqrt{2n}$ away. Customary practice is to designate the upper control limit for s as follows:

$$\text{UCL} = \bar{s} + \frac{3\bar{s}}{\hat{c}_2\sqrt{2n}} \qquad (43)$$

This formula uses $\bar{s}/\hat{c}_2$ as an estimate of σ.   The formula for this limit may be rewritten as

$$\text{UCL} = \bar{s}\left(1 + \frac{3}{\hat{c}_2\sqrt{2n}}\right) \qquad (44)$$

or

$$\text{UCL} = \hat{B}_4\bar{s} \qquad (45)$$

where

$$\hat{B}_4 = 1 + \frac{3}{\hat{c}_2\sqrt{2n}} \qquad (46)$$

Values for $\hat{B}_4$ for each possible sample size have been computed and listed in Table J.

In a like manner, the lower control limit is given by

$$LCL = \bar{s} - \frac{3\bar{s}}{\hat{c}_2 \sqrt{2n}} \tag{47}$$

which may be rewritten as

$$LCL = \bar{s} \left(1 - \frac{3}{\hat{c}_2 \sqrt{2n}} \right) \tag{48}$$

or

$$LCL = \hat{B}_3 \bar{s} \tag{49}$$

where

$$\hat{B}_3 = 1 - \frac{3}{\hat{c}_2 \sqrt{2n}} \tag{50}$$

Values for $\hat{B}_3$ will likewise be found in Table J.

Another common method of drawing the same charts, if control is found, is to regard $\bar{s}/\hat{c}_2$ as an estimate of σ, the true population standard deviation, and to substitute it for σ in the following equations. The central line is then set at $\hat{c}_2\sigma$. The upper control limit will be obtained by the formula

$$UCL = \hat{c}_2\sigma + \frac{3\sigma}{\sqrt{2n}} \tag{51}$$

or

$$UCL = \sigma \left(\hat{c}_2 + \frac{3}{\sqrt{2n}} \right) \tag{52}$$

The lower limit will be obtained by the formula

$$LCL = \hat{c}_2\sigma - \frac{3\sigma}{\sqrt{2n}} \tag{53}$$

or

$$LCL = \sigma \left(\hat{c}_2 - \frac{3}{\sqrt{2n}} \right) \tag{54}$$

If we let

$$\hat{B}_2 = \hat{c}_2 + \frac{3}{\sqrt{2n}} \tag{55}$$

and

$$\hat{B}_1 = \hat{c}_2 - \frac{3}{\sqrt{2n}} \tag{56}$$

then

$$UCL = \hat{B}_2\sigma \tag{57}$$

and

$$LCL = \hat{B}_1\sigma \tag{58}$$

$\hat{B}_2$ and $\hat{B}_1$ may easily be found from Eqs. (55) and (56) but are not tabulated in detail here, as the use of $\hat{B}_3$ and $\hat{B}_4$ is simpler and yields identical results.

It should be pointed out, in conclusion, that knowledge of control of the standard deviation must be less exact than knowledge of control over the average because the calculations for determining the limit lines are on less certain grounds. In particular, they are more dependent on the distribution of the population being normal. In addition, even if the population is normal, the distribution of the standard deviations will not be normal, although it approaches a normal distribution as n increases. For most products, however, the limits will prove practical, especially since the sample sizes used in the variables sampling plans are relatively large as subgroup sizes for control charts.

5. THE COEFFICIENT OF DISPLACEMENT

Another possible use of the control chart method is to test for the control of percent defective. This is usually the measure of quality in which the receiver of goods is essentially interested. When charts are used by the manufacturer to detect and identify assignable causes of variation at various stages in a manufacturing process, the more complete and definite information given about product variability by separate charts for averages and for measures of dispersion will be most appropriate. The user of the product, however, wants to know in most cases only the proportion of items submitted that meet the specification limits. The important fact for him to know is whether the proportion of items with measurements beyond the specification limit is or is not in control.

One customary form for charts for this purpose is to plot directly the proportion defective in samples on what is called a "p chart," p being the symbol for fraction defective. When there is little variation in the sample size n, a chart plotted in terms of the number of defectives—the pn chart—is often used. It is possible to use these two forms of charts in the analysis of data from variables acceptance plans. Readings for items in a sample can be scanned, and those beyond the specification limit, representing the defectives, noted to determine the number or proportion defective. There are serious disadvantages, however, to such a procedure. First, for the relatively small sample sizes used in the variables plans and for the general run of percent defective in industrial products, not enough defective items will turn up in the samples to make the control charts of much use. (This holds true also for a large segment of the related attribute plans.) On the p chart, for example, each limit is set a distance of

$$3 \sqrt{\bar{p} \frac{(1 - \bar{p})}{n}}$$

away from the average line $\bar{p}$ when testing for control.

If $\bar{p}$ is small and n, the sample size, is small, one can see from the formula that the limits will be quite far apart. For most installations of variables plans, the lower limit would theoretically fall a considerable distance below zero proportion defective, or, to state the consequence of a low n combined with a low $\bar{p}$ in another way, a relatively large proportion of the samples will have no defective items. This fact seriously limits the information that will be furnished by the chart.

Another serious disadvantage of considering sample items in terms of attributes when acceptance sampling inspection is by variables is that full use is not made of the information obtained by taking measurements. Variables data has been obtained for the sample and used in acceptance inspection because it tells a great deal more about the lot than attribute data; it would seem well to use the data in its variable form also for control charts for proportion defective.

One obvious way of using the variables data is to use the sample mean $\bar{x}$ as an estimate of the lot mean μ and to use the sample standard deviation s in obtaining an estimate of the lot standard deviation σ. With estimates for μ and σ one could readily find, through the procedure represented in Sec. 6.2 of Chap. 2, an estimated proportion defective for the lot. Or, as an alternative, one could work only in terms of the sample and use $\bar{x}$ and s to get a hypothetical proportion defective for the sample. These proportions could then be charted to test for control.

A much more direct procedure is recommended, however. The procedure is to plot instead for each sample the variable d which is given by the following formulas: for U an upper limit

$$d = \frac{U - \bar{x}}{s} \tag{59}$$

and for L a lower limit

$$d = \frac{\bar{x} - L}{s} \tag{60}$$

As explained in Sec. 6.2 of Chap. 2, $K = (U - \mu)/\sigma$. This is a measure for the lot of the proportion defective, the percentage of items beyond a given specification limit depending entirely on the lot mean μ and the lot standard deviation σ. The sample variable d is an estimate of the lot value K and is called the coefficient of displacement. In a control chart for d, control lines corresponding to the customary 3-sigma limits are computed and plotted on the chart. (Procedures for determining values for the control limits will be given in the next section.) For each sample, d is calculated and plotted on the chart. As long as the proportion defective is in control, values for d can be expected to fall between the limits.

In interpreting a chart for the coefficient of displacement, only one minor difference between it and a chart for p or pn need be noted; that is, a larger value for d means a smaller proportion of items defective. Hence loss of control on the low side, and not on the high side, should be the more serious cause for concern.

The control chart for the coefficient of displacement, or the d chart, as it may be called, is recommended because it has several advantages over the methods mentioned for using sample data in a variables form. First, some work is saved. Values of $\bar{x}$ and s for a sample do not have to be converted into an estimate of the proportion defective. Nothing is gained as far as knowledge of control is concerned, so there is little justification for performing this step for each sample. Second, if estimates of the proportion defective in lots were made and charts kept on this basis, the values used might be misinterpreted by some persons. These estimates are subject to sampling errors and so may vary considerably from the true value. Use of the abstract parameter d will permit no false interpretations. Third, if d is taken to statistical tables based on the normal distribution, the proportion defective given there will be true only when measurements for items are normally distributed. If the distribution deviates somewhat from normal, the charts, if kept in terms of the fraction defective, will be valid for testing for control, but control will not be at the level indicated. Charts for the coefficient of displacement will be more dependable in indicating whether or not there is control, since the distribution of values for d tends to be normal, regardless of whether or not measurement for items are normally distributed.

5.1. Calculation of Limits for the Coefficient of Displacement

$\bar{k}$ is used for the center line on the d chart. The computation of $\bar{k}$ is discussed in Sec. 6 of Chap. 5. The control limits for the d chart are computed directly and are not given by the addition and subtraction of $3\sigma_d$ to the center line as in the case of the control charts for the mean and for the standard deviation. The d-chart control limits are computed as follows:

(a) For a given value of n and $\bar{k}$, compute $\sqrt{l_2 + l_3\bar{k}^2}$; values for the constants l_2 and l_3 and for the constant l_1 whose use is indicated below are given in Table J.

(b) Compute the values for the following limits:

$$\text{UCL} = l_1\bar{k} + \sqrt{l_2 + l_3\bar{k}^2} \qquad (61)$$

$$\text{LCL} = l_1\bar{k} - \sqrt{l_2 + l_3\bar{k}^2} \qquad (62)$$

These limits correspond to the usual 3-sigma limits on the mean and standard deviation charts. It should be noted that the d-chart limits are not necessarily symmetrically placed about the line $\bar{k}$ as are the control limits on the other charts discussed. The asymmetry is due to the fact that the distribution of d is skewed whereas the normal curve, on which the mean and standard deviation charts are based, is symmetric.

5.2. Example of the Construction of a Control Chart for the Coefficient of Displacement

For this illustration, the Rockwell hardness number data given in Table 8.2 will be used. The coefficient of displacement, that is, d, is computed for each sample. Since the specification for the Rockwell hardness readings involves an upper limit, formula (59) is used to compute d:

$$d = \frac{U - \bar{x}}{s}$$

For example, the values for the mean $\bar{x}$ and for the standard deviation s for the first sample are 60.7 and 2.65, respectively. The inspection specification is a maximum reading of 68. Therefore, we obtain for d for the first sample

$$d = \frac{68 - 60.7}{2.65} = \frac{7.3}{2.65} = 2.75$$

This procedure is repeated for each sample, and the values of d thus obtained are plotted on the chart.

Sample	Coefficient of Displacement
1	2.75
2	2.91
3	2.27
4	3.10
5	2.54
6	2.29
7	2.93
8	3.74
9	2.00
10	1.55
11	2.64
12	2.49
13	2.56
14	2.63
15	2.26
16	2.34
17	1.93
18	1.96
19	2.92
20	2.19

The control chart limits are computed as outlined in the previous section.   Values for the constants l_1, l_2, l_3 and for $\bar{k}$ are needed.   For this data, the value of 2.388 for $\bar{k}$ was obtained as one of the steps in the computation of the process average.   The constants l_1, l_2, and l_3 are given in Table J.   The sampling plan used for this data specified a sample size of 25; thus, $n = 25$, and the following readings are obtained from Table J:

$$l_1 = 1.247$$
$$l_2 = 0.4535$$
$$l_3 = 0.2944$$

The value for $\sqrt{l_2 + l_3\bar{k}^2}$ is computed first.   In this problem, we obtain

$$
\begin{aligned}
\sqrt{l_2 + l_3\bar{k}^2} &= \sqrt{0.4535 + (0.2944)(2.388)^2} \\
&= \sqrt{0.4535 + (0.2944)(5.7025)} \\
&= \sqrt{0.4535 + 1.6788} \\
&= \sqrt{2.1323} \\
&= 1.460
\end{aligned}
$$

Therefore, the upper control limit is $(1.247)(2.388) + 1.460 = 4.437$, and the lower control limit is $(1.247)(2.388) - 1.460 = 1.517$.   These

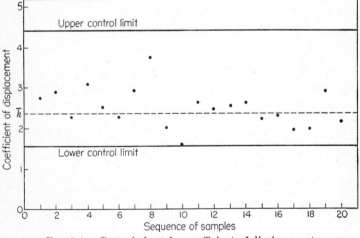

Fig. 9.1.   Control chart for coefficient of displacement.

limits are plotted on the chart, and the value of $\bar{k}$ is plotted as the "center" line as shown in Fig. 9.1.   Since all the points fall within the limits, the process is said to be in control.

CHAPTER 10

CONSTRUCTION OF SAMPLING PLANS AND STANDARD PROCEDURE

1. DESCRIPTION OF STANDARD ATTRIBUTE PROCEDURE

A standard sampling inspection procedure is a procedure for selecting and operating sampling plans. With a standard procedure, certain questions are settled arbitrarily which ordinarily are decided by an expert. For other questions the range of choice is narrowed to relatively few alternatives, with detailed prescriptions for choosing among these; some questions are analyzed into component parts, each to be decided separately by someone whose regular work gives him the competence. Since the standard procedure for variables inspection parallels in many respects the standard procedure for sampling inspection by attributes, a brief description of the standard attribute procedure will simplify our discussion. This standard procedure for attributes was prepared for the Navy during the war by the Statistical Research Group at Columbia University. The same material, with added plans and a detailed description of the principles involved in constructing a standard procedure, may be found in "Sampling Inspection."

The foundation of this standard sampling inspection procedure is, of course, a catalogue of sampling plans classified by sample-size letter (a measure of the amount of inspection required) and the acceptable quality level (the percentage of defective items for which the probability of accepting a lot containing that percentage of defective items is 0.95). The form which a summary table of such sampling plans would have is given in Fig. 10.1.

For the majority of cases covered in Fig. 10.1 (the shaded region indicates the shape of the area of coverage), single, double, and multiple (group sequential) plans are provided. For a given sample-size letter and AQL class, these three types of sampling inspection yield approximately the same OC curve. Each sample-size letter represents a fixed single-sample size and a fixed sequence of sample sizes for double and sequential sampling. Basic summary tables of this form give acceptance criteria for single, double, and sequential plans, while additional detailed tables contain, along with this information, a plot of the three OC curves for each case.

114

Although the set of tables can be used as a simple catalogue of plans, its principal purpose is to form the basis for an integrated inspection program.   An integrated inspection program requires not only the use of ready-made rather than custom-built plans, but a standard procedure for selecting a plan, separation of responsibilities for various phases of the procedure, and a systematic method for the review of current quality. In the present case, two main levels of responsibility are assumed. Decisions about quality requirements and relative amount of inspection

BASIC FORM OF SUMMARY TABLE OF SAMPLING PLANS CLASSIFIED BY SAMPLE SIZE AND AQL CLASS

Sample-size letter	Acceptable quality level class														
	0.024 to 0.035	0.035 to 0.06	0.06 to 0.12	0.12 to 0.17	0.17 to 0.22	0.22 to 0.32	0.32 to 0.65	0.65 to 1.2	1.2 to 2.2	2.2 to 3.2	3.2 to 4.4	4.4 to 5.3	5.3 to 6.4	6.4 to 8.5	8.5 to 11.0
A								—	—	—	—	—	—	—	
B							—	—	—	—	—	—	—	—	
C							—	—	—	—	—	—	—	—	
D					—	—	—	—	—	—	—	—	—	—	
E					—	—	—	—	—	—	—	—	—		
F				—	—	—	—	—	—	—	—	—	—		
G			—	—	—	—	—	—	—	—	—	—	—		
H		—	—	—	—	—	—	—	—	—	—	—	—		
I		—	—	—	—	—	—	—	—	—	—	—			
J	—	—	—	—	—	—	—	—	—	—	—	—			—
K	—	—	—	—	—	—	—	—	—	—	—	—			—
L	—	—	—	—	—	—	—	—	—	—	—	—			
M	—	—	—	—	—	—	—	—	—	—	—				
N	—	—	—	—	—	—	—	—	—						
O	—	—	—	—	—	—	—								

FIG. 10.1.

are made by an executive who has general responsibility; decisions about administrative features of individual plans, such as type of sampling to use, are made by the inspection supervisor.   The standard procedure consists of 14 steps grouped into four major categories: (a) establishment of standards, (b) installation of procedure, (c) operation of procedure, and (d) review of past results; (a) and (d) are associated with the first level of responsibility, and (b) and (c) with the other.

2. CONSTRUCTION OF PARALLEL VARIABLES PLANS

In constructing a standard procedure for variables inspection, a fundamental question arose as to whether to cover the appropriate range of lot sizes, acceptable quality levels, and average outgoing-quality levels by a new systematic set of variables plans or to try to match the individual operating characteristic curves in the attribute tables. It was decided to construct a set of variables plans matching the existing attribute OC curves, since this would allow the use of the attribute and variables plans on a parallel basis. It appeared that the number of items inspected could be chosen so that the relation between lot size and sample size is consistent with the attribute plans and still achieve considerable saving in the number of observations. A detailed description of the degree of match between these plans will be given in the next section.

Of course, the same general criterion for classifying sampling plans is as appropriate to variables inspection as to attribute inspection, since in both cases quality is characterized by percent defective. The basic classification is by acceptable quality level and sample-size letter. Detailed discussion of the reasons for selecting these two criteria is given in Chap. 15 of "Sampling Inspection." Briefly, the reason for selecting AQL as the particular measure of the protection afforded by a sampling plan was to ensure uniform treatment of all suppliers. A sample-size letter was chosen as a measure of the cost of inspection because this cost is very closely related to the number of items inspected. The number of items inspected is, of course, the same for all single-sampling plans with the same sample-size letter; the expected number of observations differs for the double-sampling plans, but the sample-size letter is still a good measure of the relative amount of inspection for different plans with the same AQL. Furthermore, the procedure of defining AQL by range rather than a point was taken directly from the attribute procedures.

Since these variables plans have many features in common with the standard attribute procedure, it is possible to consolidate the attribute and variables procedures into one standard procedure. The steps of the standard procedure relating to the establishment of acceptance standards are common to both plans. These steps include:

1. Decide what shall be an item of product.
2. List and classify defects.
3. Fix AQL for each class of defect.
4. Decide on an inspection level.

Furthermore, the next step in the standard procedure—the formation of the inspection lots—is also the same for variables and attribute inspection. However, the next two steps in the installation—decide what type of sampling shall be used and select a sampling plan for each class of defect—would be modified in the composite procedure. In the attribute standard procedure, the decision made at this stage is whether to use single, double, or sequential sampling. In the variables standard procedure, the decision is between single and double sampling. In the composite standard procedure, there would clearly be five possibilities. The basic decision between variables and attribute inspection would be followed by the selection of the particular type of sampling. Once the type of sampling plan has been chosen, it is necessary to extract the acceptance criteria from the appropriate table. If an attribute plan were used, Table 2 [2(a), 2(b), or 2(c)] of "Sampling Inspection" would be used. The corresponding tables for variables inspection in this book are Table B for single-sampling variables plans and Table C for double-sampling variables plans.

The next three steps in the standard procedure deal with the operation of the procedure in each individual application. The first step—selection of sample items from each inspection lot—would be common to both variables and attributes. The next step—the inspection of individual sample items—would be effected only in that numerical measurements would be recorded for the variables scheme. Of course, the final decision of acceptance or rejection would be based on different calculations. The attribute procedure is discussed on page 103 of "Sampling Inspection." The variables procedure is described in Chap. 5, Secs. 3 and 4, of this book.

As far as review of past results is concerned, the two steps require different calculations but are fundamentally the same. After the process average is computed, it is referred to a table of upper and lower limits to decide whether to apply tightened or reduced inspection. For attribute inspection this table is Table 11.5 in "Sampling Inspection" and for variables inspection is Table H in this book.

To summarize, the standard attribute procedure used by the Navy and described in "Sampling Inspection" and the standard procedure for variables described in this book can easily be merged, since essentially they consist of the same steps. Some of the steps are carried out in exactly the same way, particularly those dealing with the establishment of standards. In the installation and operation of the procedure and in a review of past results, the actual successive steps are the same, but the details of carrying out the application, computations and the tables required, are different.

3. CONSTRUCTION OF SINGLE-SAMPLING VARIABLES PLANS AND THE MATCH BETWEEN THE ATTRIBUTE AND VARIABLES PLANS

The basic problem in the construction of single-sampling plans was to pick a sample size for a variables plan which would match as closely as possible the attribute plans. A plot of the lot tolerance percent defective versus the acceptable quality level was made for each of the various sample-size letters of the attribute plans.   Each curve was drawn through points representing possible single-sampling plans for a fixed number of observations.   Only a finite number of plans are possible because the acceptance number must be an integer.   Similar curves for various numbers of observations for variables plans were drawn on this grid.   If one of the lines in the variables plans coincided exactly with the attribute line, a perfect match was obtained.   Since the slope increases with the number of observations, it is hard to get a good match all along the line for large sample sizes.   Figure 10.2 shows the LTPD plotted against the AQL for sample-size letter H of the attribute plans corresponding to a

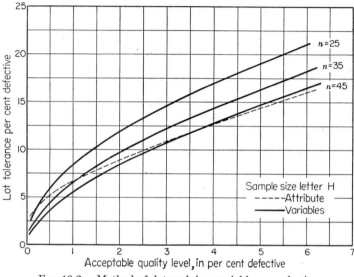

FIG. 10.2.   Method of determining variables sample size.

sample size of 75.   Superimposed are curves representing variables plans with sample sizes 25, 35, and 45.   Thus, it is seen that variables plans corresponding to many different sample sizes intersect the attribute line. A value was chosen so that the match was best in the middle range of the AQL classes covered by a sample-size letter.   Thus, for the sample-size letter H for the variables plans, a sample size of 35 was chosen. Under this choice, all values of the AQL and the LTPD except for one pair are within 5 and 4 percent, respectively, of the corresponding attribute values.

Because of the continuous nature of variables, it is possible to construct plans for the smaller AQL classes in situations in which no single-sampling attribute plan exists.   There are 163 variables cases, of which 129 correspond to attribute cases.   In all cases, the AQL of the variables

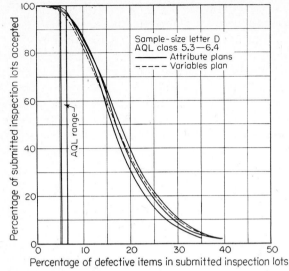

FIG. 10.3.   Match between attribute and variables plans when the attribute AQL's are outside established AQL range.

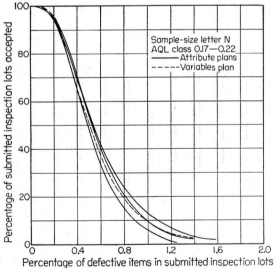

FIG. 10.4.   Example of a good match between attribute and variables sampling plans.

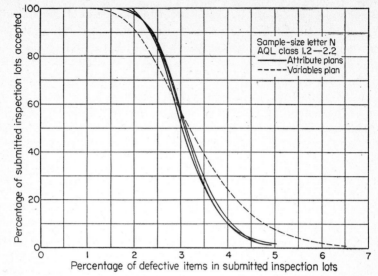

Fig. 10.5.   Example of a bad match between attribute and variables sampling plans.

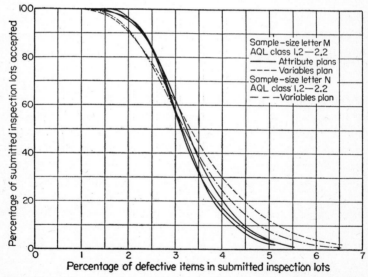

Fig. 10.6.   Example of a bad match between attribute and variables sampling plans showing use of a larger sample size to obtain a closer match.

plan falls within the AQL class; this is not always true of the attribute plans (see Fig. 10.3). For most of the cases there are three attribute curves—single, double, and sequential—which do not match exactly. Of the 129 variables cases which have corresponding attribute plans, 60 have the variables AQL within the range of the three attribute AQL's. The AQL's of 53 plans depart from the closest attribute AQL's by 10 percent or less. The remaining 16 curves may be considered relatively poorer matches. The situation at the LTPD (10 percent point) is somewhat less favorable. Actually, in constructing the plans, the AQL was given preference over the LTPD. However, 27 of the cases are within the three attribute curves and an additional 84 depart from the closest attribute LTPD by 15 percent or less. On the whole, the matching is satisfactory, and most of the plans could be incorporated in the attribute plans. Examples of good and bad matches are given in Figs. 10.4 and 10.5. Even for the bad match, the difference in AQL between the variables plan and the attribute plan is only about 40 percent of the AQL class. In including the variables plans on a parallel basis, it may be sensible to omit some of the bad matches and to recommend the use of a different sample-size letter (see Fig. 10.6).

4. CONSTRUCTION OF DOUBLE-SAMPLING PLANS

The first problem to be faced in the construction of double-sampling plans was the problem of picking the first and second sample size in some optimal way. In the Navy and Statistical Research Group attribute tables, the second sample size is always double the first, a feature which was borrowed from the Army Service Forces and Dodge-Romig tables, from which many of the double-sampling plans were taken. It has been pointed out by several people that double-sampling plans can be selected such that the expected number of observations at the AQL is smaller than the expected number of observations in the current plans. It is difficult to establish double-sampling plans which are best for all problems. In any case, if the distribution of presented quality were known, the realized average amount of inspection could be minimized. While the distribution of presented quality is highly variable for different products, certain features of it do stand out. The overwhelming majority of cases in which sampling inspection is applied result in the acceptance of a lot and correspond to presented qualities much better than the acceptable quality level. In fact, the sampling inspection program forces the supplier to submit quality better than the AQL. In general, the first sample size—for a double-sampling plan which minimizes the expected number of observations at the AQL—will be larger than the first sample size of the double-sampling plan with the same risks which has the second sample size twice the first. The expected number of observations in the region of most interest (between O and the AQL) will be closer to this first sample size. Consequently, the total amount of inspection realized will usually be smaller for the double-sampling plan which has a smaller first sample size. Features which tend to make the first sample size large are the expected number of observations at the rejectable quality level and the necessity for accumulating information for quality control purposes. It appears that the two-to-one ratio is a fairly reasonable compromise between the various factors involved.

The second problem in connection with double-sampling plans was to obtain methods for calculating the risks. The joint distribution of two non-central t's (see Chap. 11, Secs. 1.2 and 2.2), one based on the first n_1 observations and the other based on a total of N observations including the first n_1, was derived. It is a very complicated bivariate distribution function, but it was feasible to use it for the smaller n_1 and N to evaluate risks and the expected number of observations. For larger values of n_1 and N, a generalization of the well-known one-dimensional approximation was used. That is, in one dimension the distribution of $\bar{x} + ks$ is much closer to the normal than the non-central t itself is. Similarly, the joint distribution of $\bar{x}_1 + k_a s_1$ and $\bar{x}_t + k_t s_t$ is fairly well approximated by a bivariate normal distribution. Details are given in Chap. 11.

5. SEQUENTIAL METHODS

For various reasons, it was decided not to construct item-by-item sequential plans for compilation into the standard variables procedure. The basic reason for this is the elaborate computation required to apply these plans (roughly equivalent to computing a t statistic after each observation). In addition, there are a number of theoretical questions which should be cleared up before a set of standard sampling plans is prepared.

6. ADJUSTMENT OF SAMPLING PLANS

A detailed discussion of the principles of adjustment of sampling plans may be found in "Sampling Inspection," Chap. 16, page 177. The application of these principles to the variables inspection for fraction defective is discussed in Chap. 5 of this book. Briefly, the idea is to make some adjustment in the sampling plan if such adjustment is called for by the submitted quality. The standard procedure for selecting a plan does not consider quality of product submitted, except in so far as this affects the selection of the AQL class. Often the AQL class is chosen in terms of quality requirements, rather than quality attainable.

It is clear that, if we knew exactly the distribution of presented quality, we could choose a sampling plan which would discriminate between lots and be efficient from the point of view of requiring very little inspection. For example, if we knew that the percentage of defective items in all submitted lots was less than the AQL, we could simply accept all lots without any inspection. Similarly, if we knew that an unacceptable number of defectives was present in all submitted lots, we could reject all lots without inspection. The optimum action to take if we actually had a distribution of presented quality might be very complicated to characterize, but it is clear that the stringency of our plan would depend on this presented quality.

The introduction of the notion of reduced and tightened inspection represents a rather crude and admittedly arbitrary method of adjusting the sampling plan to submitted quality. If it can be established that the product submitted is of generally high quality, then it is relatively less important to sort lots according to quality. A sampling plan requiring an amount of inspection less than the normal will serve to give information on quality and to protect against a sudden deterioration. On the other hand, if lots submitted are generally unacceptable, it is clear that the present sampling plan, even though it results in a substantial number of rejects, does not provide adequate incentive for the supplier to improve his quality. Consequently, a plan with a lower (that is, stiffer) AQL is imposed.

Because of the variation inherent in industrial processes the decisions to reduce and tighten inspection should be subject to regular review. To justify reduced inspection, it must be assumed that the producer will continue to supply high quality, and consequently, reasonable precaution should be taken to see that the product is being produced under essentially the same conditions. In addition to the empirical fact that the percent defective is smaller than the AQL class specified, it is required that the last 20 lots submitted under normal inspection have all been accepted and that production and submission of the item be continuous. Furthermore, normal inspection will be resumed immediately if an inspection lot is rejected through operation of the reduced sampling plan, if the process average exceeds the upper value limiting the selected AQL class, or if production or purchase of the item has been interrupted.

Since the tightened inspection actually increases protection of the consumer and since the sample size is not increased, it does not increase the inspection cost. Tightened inspection is continued until a new process average shows definite improvement. When the submitted product improves in quality so that the process average has a value equal to or less than the larger figure defining the desired AQL class, normal inspection may be resumed.

The limits on process average are given in Table H, depending on the AQL class and on the number of sample items from which the process average is computed. The upper limits are computed so that, if the true percent defective were equal to the larger of the two values defining the AQL class, the specified process average would be equal to or exceed the upper limit only one time in forty. Thus, there is at most one chance in forty that the criterion for tightened inspection will be satisfied when tightened inspection should not be used. The lower limit for the AQL class is determined in a similar way.

For low AQL classes a process average based on a small number of observations may not give enough assurance that reduced or tightened inspection will be used when they are appropriate. For any AQL class, the minimum number of items for the computation of a process average and subsequent decision about reduced or tightened inspection corresponds to the first entry in Table H under the AQL class.

CHAPTER 11

THE MATHEMATICS OF SAMPLING INSPECTION BY VARIABLES

1. SINGLE-SAMPLING PLANS

As indicated in Chap. 2, Sec. 6, the basic assumption of the variables plans is that the item qualities follow a normal law. Let μ be the mean and σ^2 the variance of this distribution. Then the statement that a specified proportion p of the population lies above a limit U is equivalent to saying that $\mu = U - K_p\sigma$ where

$$\frac{1}{\sqrt{2\pi}} \int_{K_p}^{\infty} e^{-t^2/2}\, dt = p$$

1.1. Known Standard Deviation

We want to devise acceptance procedures for a given n chosen as indicated in Chap. 10 such that, if $p = p_1$, the probability of rejecting a lot is α (where α is taken as 0.05 in the plans presented in the book). The larger p, the proportion defective, the larger μ; we are interested in rejecting the lot if μ is large. For known sigma, our critical region is to reject if $\bar{x}$ exceeds a given constant; in particular, if $\bar{x} > U - k'\sigma$ where

$$k' = K_{p_1} - \frac{K_\alpha}{\sqrt{n'}}$$

and n' is the sample size for known standard deviation plans. The probability L_p of accepting a lot with a given proportion defective p, that is, the OC curve of this plan, is

$$L_p = \int_{-\infty}^{\sqrt{n'}(K_p - k')} \frac{e^{-t^2/2}}{\sqrt{2\pi}}\, dt$$

1.2. Unknown Standard Deviation

In the case of unknown sigma, the most powerful test procedure for $p = p_1$ against alternatives of the form $p \geq p_1$ is to reject if $\bar{x} + ks > U$. To calculate k, note that $\sqrt{n}[(U - \bar{x})/s]$ has the non-central t distribution; that is,

$$p(t|f,K_p) = \frac{f! f^{f/2}}{2^{f-\frac{1}{2}}\Gamma(f/2)} \frac{1}{(f+t^2)^{(f+1)/2}} e^{-[f(f+1)K_p^2]/[2(f+t^2)]} Hh_f\left(-\frac{t\sqrt{f+1}\,K_p}{\sqrt{f+t^2}}\right)$$

where
$$Hh_f(x) = \int_0^\infty e^{-\frac{1}{2}(v+x)^2}\frac{v^f}{f!}\,dv$$

and $f = n - 1$. The test procedure uses a k such that

$$\int_{-\infty}^{\sqrt{n}k} p(t|n-1, K_{p_1})dt = \alpha$$

The best available tables of the non-central t distribution are provided by Johnson and Welch.[†] Essentially they give a table of K_p defined as a function of t_0 by the equation

$$\int_{t_0}^\infty p(t|f,K_p)dt = \epsilon$$

for fixed ϵ and f. (We use $\sqrt{n}\,K_p$ instead of the Johnson and Welch symbol δ.) Actually tables of λ are given with λ a function of y_0 and K_p where $y_0 = [1 + (t_0^2/2f)]^{-\frac{1}{2}}$ and $\sqrt{n}\,K_p = t_0 - (\lambda/y_0)$. Detailed directions for obtaining k and the OC curve from these tables are given in "Techniques of Statistical Analysis," Chap. 1, Sec. 11.4. This procedure involves successive approximations to k. The first approximation, introduced by Jennett and Welch,[‡] is a normal approximation obtained by assuming that $\bar{x} + ks$ is normally distributed with mean $\mu + k\sigma$ and variance $\sigma^2\{1/n + [k^2/2(n-1)]\}$. The normal approximation to k is

$$k = \frac{\sqrt{n}\,K_{p_1} + K_\alpha\sqrt{1 + [K_{p_1}^2/2(n-1)] - [K_\alpha^2/2(n-1)]}}{\sqrt{n}\,\{1 - [K_\alpha^2/2(n-1)]\}}$$

Using this same normal approximation, the OC curve L_p may be found from

$$K_{L_p} = \frac{k - K_p}{\sqrt{(1/n) + [k^2/2(n-1)]}}$$

where K_{L_p} is the normal deviate exceeded with probability L_p. This normal approximation is also discussed in detail in Chap. 1 of "Techniques of Statistical Analysis."[§]

[†] N. L. Johnson and B. L. Welch, "Applications of the Non-central t-Distribution," *Biometrika*, Vol. 31, pp. 362–389, 1940.

[‡] W. J. Jennett and B. L. Welch, "The Control of Proportion Defective as Judged by a Single Quality Characteristic Varying on a Continuous Scale," *Supplement to the Journal of the Royal Statistical Society*, Vol. VI, pp. 80–88, 1939.

[§] Statistical Research Group, Columbia University, "Techniques of Statistical Analysis," McGraw-Hill Book Company, Inc., New York, 1947.

An expansion of the probability integral of the non-central t in a series of incomplete-beta functions due to C. C. Craig[†] was also useful, especially for small f.   It is easy to show by his method that

$$\int_{-\infty}^{t_0} p(t|f,\delta)dt = \frac{e^{-\delta^2/2}}{2} \sum_{r=0}^{\infty} \frac{(-1)^r(\delta^2/2)^{r/2}}{\Gamma[(r/2)+1]}\left[1 - I_{\frac{t_0^2}{f+t_0^2}}\left(\frac{r+1}{2},\frac{f}{2}\right)\right]$$

2. DOUBLE-SAMPLING PLANS

2.1. Known Standard Deviation Plans

In the case of known standard deviation, the OC curve and expected sample size associated with double-sampling plans are based on the bivariate normal distribution.   Recall that a double-sampling plan is of the following sort: Draw a sample of size n_1'.   If $\bar{x}_1 + k_a'\sigma \leq U$, accept the lot; if $\bar{x}_1 + k_r'\sigma \geq U$, reject the lot.   Otherwise draw a second sample of size n_2'.   If $\bar{x}_t + k_a'\sigma \leq U$, accept the lot; otherwise reject the lot. Since $\bar{x}_1$ is normally distributed, the probability of accepting and rejecting on the first sample $[P(A_1)$ and $P(R_1)]$ may be computed from tables of the normal integral as follows:

$$P(A_1) = \frac{1}{\sqrt{2\pi}}\int_{-\infty}^{\sqrt{n_1'}(K_p - k_a')} e^{-t^2/2}dt$$

and
$$P(R_1) = \frac{1}{\sqrt{2\pi}}\int_{\sqrt{n_1'}(K_p - k_r')}^{\infty} e^{-t^2/2}dt$$

Since $\bar{x}_t$ is the mean of the first $n_1' + n_2'$ observations, it is correlated with $\bar{x}_1$; the correlation coefficient is $\rho = \sqrt{n_1'/(n_1'+n_2')}$ which is $1/\sqrt{3}$ if $n_2' = 2n_1'$.   Let $n_1' + n_2' = N'$, the total number of observations if first and second samples are taken.   The probability $P(A_2)$ of accepting on the second sample is given by

$$P(A_2) = \frac{1}{2\pi}\sqrt{\frac{N'}{n_2'}}\int_{-\infty}^{\sqrt{N'}(K_p - k_t')}\int_{\sqrt{n_1'}(K_p - k_a')}^{\sqrt{n_1'}(K_p - k_r')} e^{-N'/2n_2'(u^2 - 2\sqrt{n_1'/N'}uv + v^2)}du\ dv$$

The OC curve then is
$$L_p = P(A_1) + P(A_2)$$
and the ASN is
$$n' + [1 - P(A_1) - P(R_1)]n_2'$$

$P(A_2)$ was taken from Pearson's tables of volumes under the normal bivariate surface.[‡]   Procedures for the choice of the constants will be discussed in Sec. 2.4.

[†] C. C. Craig, "Note on the Distribution of Non-central t with an Application," *Annals of Mathematical Statistics*, Vol. XII, pp. 224–228, 1941.

[‡] Karl Pearson, "Tables for Statisticians and Biometricians," Part II, Cambridge University Press, London.

2.2. Unknown Standard Deviation Plans

In this case the form of the sampling plan is as follows: Draw a sample of size n_1, and accept if $\bar{x}_1 + k_a s_1 \leq U$; reject if $\bar{x}_1 + k_r s_1 > U$. Otherwise draw a second sample of size n_2, and accept if $\bar{x}_t + k_t s_t \leq U$; reject otherwise. The probabilities of accepting and rejecting on the first sample are given by areas under the non-central t distribution:

$$P(A_1) = \int_{-\infty}^{\sqrt{n_1}k_a} p(t|n_1 - 1, K_p)dt$$

and

$$P(R_1) = \int_{\sqrt{n_1}k_r}^{\infty} p(t|n_1 - 1, K_p)dt$$

To calculate the probability of accepting on the second sample, it was necessary to derive the joint distribution of two non-central t statistics, one based on the first sample and the other on the total sample.

We make the following definitions:

$$N = n_1 + n_2$$

$$\bar{x}_1 = \frac{\sum_{i=1}^{n_1} x_i}{n_1}$$

$$s_1^2 = \frac{\sum_{i=1}^{n_1} (x_i - \bar{x}_1)^2}{n_1 - 1}$$

$$\bar{x}_2 = \frac{\sum_{j=1}^{n_2} x_j}{n_2}$$

$$s_2^2 = \frac{\sum_{j=1}^{n_2} (x_j - \bar{x}_2)^2}{n_2 - 1}$$

$$\bar{x}_t = \frac{\sum_{i=1}^{N} x_i}{N} = \frac{n_1\bar{x}_1 + n_2\bar{x}_2}{N}$$

$$s_t^2 = \frac{\sum_{i=1}^{N} (x_i - \bar{x})^2}{N - 1}$$

If we let $t_1 = \sqrt{n_1}\,\bar{x}_1/s_1$ and $t_2 = \sqrt{N}\,\bar{x}_t/s_t$, it can be shown that the joint distribution is given by the following:

Case I

$$p(t_1, t_2 | n_1, N, K_p) = C_1 \frac{(\gamma + \alpha^{1/2})^{(N+n_1-3)/2} \alpha^{(N-n_1-3)/4}}{\beta^{(N+n_1-3)/2} (N - 1 + t_2^2)^{N/2}} e^{\frac{1}{2} \frac{N(N-1)K_p^2}{N-1+t_2^2}}$$

$$\cdot Hh_{N-1} \left(\frac{-\sqrt{N} K_p t_2}{\sqrt{N - 1 + t_2^2}} \right) F \left(\frac{-N + n_1 + 3}{2}, \frac{N - n_1 - 1}{2}, \frac{N + n_1 - 1}{2}; \frac{\gamma + \alpha^{1/2}}{2\alpha^{1/2}} \right)$$

Case II

$$p(t_1, t_2 | n_1, N, K_p) = C_2 \frac{\gamma^{n_1-1} \alpha^{(N-n_1-2)/2}}{\beta^{(N+n_1-3)/2} (N - 1 + t_2^2)^{N/2}} e^{-\frac{1}{2} \left(\frac{N(N-1)K_p^2}{N-1+t_2^2} \right)}$$

$$\cdot Hh_{N-1} \left(\frac{-\sqrt{N} K_p t_2}{\sqrt{N - 1 + t_2^2}} \right) F \left(\frac{1 - n_1}{2}, \frac{2 - n_1}{2}, \frac{N - n_1}{2}; \frac{\alpha}{\gamma^2} \right)$$

where

$$C_1 = \frac{\sqrt{N} \, \Gamma(N)(N - 1)^{(N-1)/2} \Gamma(n_1)}{\sqrt{n_1 - 1} \sqrt{n_2} \, \Gamma \left(\frac{n_1 - 1}{2} \right) \Gamma \left(\frac{N + n_1 - 1}{2} \right) \pi 2^{(n_1-1)/2}}$$

$$C_2 = \frac{\sqrt{N} \, \Gamma(N)(N - 1)^{(N-1)/2}}{\sqrt{n_1 - 1} \sqrt{n_2} \, \Gamma[(n_1 - 1)/2] \sqrt{\pi} \, 2^{(N-4)/2}}$$

$$\alpha = 1 - \frac{n_1 t_2^2}{n_2(N - 1)} + \frac{N t_1^2}{n_2(n_1 - 1)}$$

$$\beta = 1 + \frac{N t_1^2}{n_2(n_1 - 1)}$$

$$\gamma = \frac{\sqrt{n_1 N} \, t_1 t_2}{n_2 \sqrt{(n_1 - 1)(N - 1)}}$$

$$F(a, b, c; z) = 1 + \frac{ab}{c} z + \frac{a(a + 1)b(b + 1)}{c(c + 1)} \frac{z^2}{2!} + \cdots$$

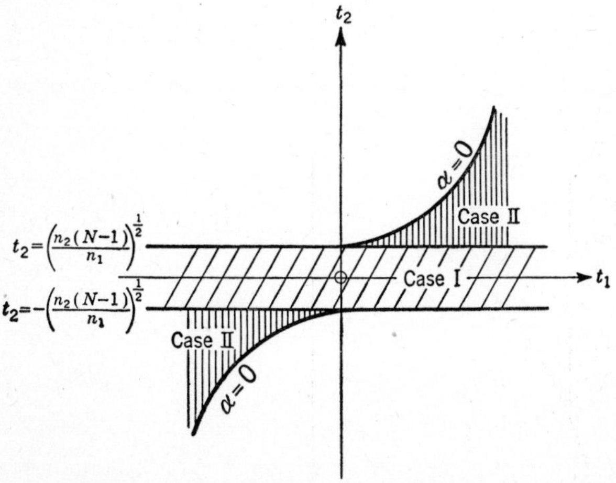

FIG. 11.1. Region of integration for the distribution of two non-central t statistics.

The region for which Case I applies is $|t_2| < [n_2(N - 1)/n_1]^{1/2}$, and the region for which Case II applies is $\alpha \geq 0$, $t_1 t_2 > 0$ and $|t_2| > [n_2(N - 1)/n_1]^{1/2}$. These regions are illustrated in Fig. 11.1. The probability of accepting on the second sample is the integral of this distribution over the region indicated by the inequalities $\sqrt{n_1}\, k_a \leq t_1 \leq \sqrt{n_1}\, k_r$ and $t_2 \leq \sqrt{N}\, k_t$ and by the natural boundaries of this distribution.

Actually, the direct integration of these formulas was carried out only for selected cases as explained in Sec. 2.4. A typical example is the case $n_1 = 5$, $n_2 = 10$. For this example we find for Case II:

$$p(t_1, t_2 | 5, 15, K_p) = \frac{\sqrt{3}\ \Gamma(15)(14)^7}{\Gamma(5)2^7 \cdot \pi} \frac{\gamma^4 \alpha^4}{\beta^{17/2}} \left(\frac{1}{14 + t_2^2}\right)^{15/2} e^{-\frac{105 K_p^2}{14 + t_2^2}}$$

$$\cdot\ Hh_{14}\left(\frac{-15 t_2 K_p}{\sqrt{14 + t_2^2}}\right) F\left(-2, -\frac{3}{2}, 5; \frac{\alpha}{\gamma^2}\right)$$

where $\alpha = 1 - \dfrac{t_2^2}{28} + \dfrac{3 t_1^2}{8}$

$\beta = 1 + \dfrac{3 t_1^2}{8}$

$\gamma = \dfrac{3}{4\sqrt{14}}\, t_1 t_2$

$F\left(-2, -\dfrac{3}{2}, 5; \dfrac{\alpha}{\gamma^2}\right) = 1 + \dfrac{3}{5}\dfrac{\alpha}{\gamma^2} + \dfrac{\alpha^2}{40\gamma^2}$

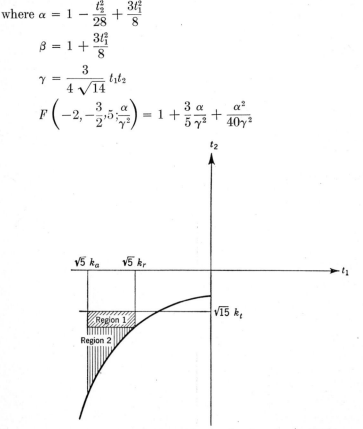

Fig. 11.2. Region of integration for $p(t_1, t_2 | 5, 15, K_p)$.

and the region of integration is the shaded region in Figure 11.2.

Let
$$h(t_1,t_2) = \frac{\gamma^4\alpha^4}{\beta^{17/2}} F\left(-2,-\frac{3}{2},5;\frac{\alpha}{\gamma^2}\right)$$

and $\;f(t_2) = \dfrac{\sqrt{3}\,\Gamma(15)(14)^7}{\Gamma(5)2^7\cdot\pi}\left(\dfrac{1}{14+t_2^2}\right)^{15/2} e^{-\frac{105K_p^2}{14+t_2^2}} Hh_{14}\left(\dfrac{-15t_2K_p}{\sqrt{14+t_2^2}}\right)$

therefore,
$$p(t_1,t_2|5,15,K_p) = h(t_1,t_2)f(t_2)$$

Then the probability of accepting on the second sample is given by

$$\int_{-\infty}^{\sqrt{N}k_t}\int_{R_{t_1}} p(t_1,t_2|5,15,K_p)dt_1\,dt_2 = \int_{-\infty}^{\sqrt{N}k_t} f(t_2)\left[\int_{R_{t_1}} h(t_1,t_2)\,dt_1\right]dt_2$$

where the range of integration on t_1, R_{t_1}, is region 1 from $\sqrt{5}\,k_a$ to $-\sqrt{8/3[(t_2^2/28)-1]}$ and region 2 from $\sqrt{5}\,k_a$ to $\sqrt{5}\,k_r$. $\int_{R_{t_1}} h(t_1,t_2)dt_1$ can be evaluated by elementary methods; $\int_{R_{t_1}} h(t_1,t_2) = H(t_2,z_u) - H(t_2,z_l)$ where z_u is the value of t_1 at the upper limit of R_{t_1} and z_l is the value of t_1 at the lower limit of R_{t_1} and

$$H(t_2,z) = \sqrt{\frac{2}{3}}\left[\frac{1}{20}\left(z-\frac{z^3}{3}\right) - \frac{3t_2^2}{10\cdot 28}\,(z-2z^3+z^5)\right.$$

$$+ \frac{t_2^4}{4\cdot 28^2}\,(3z-11z^3+13z^5-5z^7)$$

$$- \frac{t_2^6}{15\cdot 28^3}\,(15z-80z^3+150z^5-120z^7+35z^9)$$

$$+ \frac{t_2^8}{4\cdot 28^4}\,(3z-21z^3+54z^5-66z^7+39z^9-9z^{11})$$

$$- \frac{t_2^{10}}{10\cdot 28^5}\,(3z-26z^3+85z^5-140z^7+125z^9-58z^{11}+11z^{13})$$

$$\left.+ \frac{t_2^{12}}{60\cdot 28^6}\,(3z-31z^3+123z^5-255z^7+305z^9-213z^{11}+81z^{13}-13z^{15})\right]$$

Therefore, the probability of accepting in the second sample in this case is

$$\int_{-\infty}^{\sqrt{N}k_t} f(t_2)[H(t_2,z_u) - H(t_2,z_l)]dt_2$$

The integration on t_2 was performed numerically.

2.3. Approximation by a Bivariate Normal Integral

For large values of n_1 and N, the evaluation of the probability integral of two non-central t statistics becomes cumbersome, and it is possible to approximate this probability by a bivariate normal integral. In analogy with the single variables case, we consider the joint distribution of $\bar{x}_1 + k_a s_1$ and $\bar{x}_t + k_t s_t$. We are interested in calculating

$$P(\sqrt{n_1}\, k_a \leq t_1 \sqrt{n_1}\, k_r,\ t_2 \leq \sqrt{N}\, k_t)$$
$$= P(t_1 \leq \sqrt{n_1}\, k_r,\ t_2 \leq \sqrt{N}\, k_t) - P(t_1 \leq \sqrt{n_1}\, k_a,\ t_2 \leq \sqrt{N}\, k_t)$$

Now $P(t_1 \leq \sqrt{n_1}\, k_a,\ t_2 \leq \sqrt{N}\, k_t) = P(\bar{x}_1 + k_a s_1 \leq 0,\ \bar{x}_t + k_t s_t \leq 0)$

which for large n and N is approximately

$$\int_{-\infty}^{-E(U)/\sigma_U} \int_{-\infty}^{-E(V)/\sigma_V} \frac{1}{2\pi(1-\rho)^{\frac{1}{2}}}\, e^{-\frac{1}{2(1-\rho^2)}(u^2 - 2\rho uv + v^2)}\, du\, dv$$

where $E(V) = -K_p - \dfrac{\sqrt{n_1}\, k_a}{\sqrt{n_1 - 1}}$

$\quad\quad\ E(U) = -K_p - \dfrac{\sqrt{N}\, k_t}{\sqrt{N - 1}}$

$\quad\quad\ \sigma_V^2 = \dfrac{1}{n_1} + \dfrac{k_a^2}{2(n_1 - 1)}, \quad\quad \sigma_U^{2} = \dfrac{1}{N} + \dfrac{k_t^2}{2(N - 1)}$

$\quad\quad\ \sigma_{UV} = \dfrac{1}{N} + k_a k_t \left(1 - \dfrac{1}{4n_1} - \dfrac{7}{32n_1^2}\right)\left(\dfrac{1}{2N} + \dfrac{1}{2N^2} + \dfrac{5}{16N^3}\right)$

$\quad\quad\ \rho = \dfrac{\sigma_{UV}}{\sigma_U \sigma_V}$

A similar expression holds for $P(t_1 \leq \sqrt{n_1}\, k_r, t_2 \leq \sqrt{N}\, k_t)$.

2.4. Selection of Constants for Double-sampling Plans

For sample-size letters H through O which correspond to sample sizes $n_1 = 15$, $N = 45$ for H and $n_1 = 85$, $N = 255$ for O, the normal approximation to the distribution of both one and two non-central t statistics was used. The values of n_1 were selected on the basis of the corresponding single-sample sizes, and N was taken as $3n_1$, the second sample always being twice as large as the first. Values of k_a, k_r, and k_t were chosen by trial and error, but indications of their values were given as follows: $k_a \sim -K_{p_1}$, $k_r \sim -K_{p_2}$, $k_t \sim -\frac{1}{2}(K_{p_1} + K_{p_2})$. The probability of accepting at p_1 and at p_2 was computed for a given set k_a, k_r, k_t, and if the probabilities equaled 0.95 and 0.10, respectively, that set of constants k_a, k_r, k_t was considered satisfactory, subject only to the requirement that the average sample size at p_1 be less than or equal to the average sample size at p_2. For each sample-size letter, it was noticed that the expected sample size at p_1 and at p_2 clustered about the same value and that the values for the constants k_a, k_r, k_t were monotonic over the range of AQL classes.

For sample-size letters B through G which correspond to sample sizes $n_1 = 4$, $N = 12$ for B and $n_1 = 10$, $N = 30$ for G, the sampling plans were computed as follows. Values of k_a, k_r, and k_t were chosen as indicated above. The probabilities for the first sample were computed using the t tables, and the normal approximation was used for the second sample probabilities. Then for two or three selected cases for each sample-size letter, a numerical integration was performed to compute the probabilities for the second sample from the exact distribution function of two non-central t statistics. On the basis of these two or three cases, the difference between the approximate and the exact values of the probabilities for the entire range of each sample letter was inferred and the remainder of the cases were computed using the exact t tables for the first sample and the normal approximation for the second, but allowing for the expected error in the normal approximation. (For sample letter B, it was necessary to use Craig's series expansion for the probability integral of non-central t, since the published tables of t did not give a value of f small enough.)

Similar procedures were followed for the selection of k'_a, k'_r, and k'_t for the known standard deviation plans.

3. TWO-SIDED TESTS

As indicated in Chap. 7, the plans presented in this book for use with two-sided specification limits are based on two one-sided criteria. For these plans, an item is considered defective if it lies above an upper specification limit U or below a lower specification limit L. We cannot now make the statement (as was done for single-limit plans) that there is a unique proportion defective corresponding to a given mean μ and variance σ^2 of the normal distribution describing item quality. For two-sided specification limits, there are an infinity of pairs (μ,σ) corresponding to a given proportion defective p; each pair (μ,σ) determines a division of p into p' and p'' where p' is the proportion defective lying below L and $p'' = p - p'$ lying above U.

Thus
$$\int_{-\infty}^{L} \frac{1}{\sqrt{2\pi}\,\sigma}\, e^{-\frac{1}{2}[(x-\mu)/\sigma]^2} dx + \int_{U}^{\infty} \frac{1}{\sqrt{2\pi}\,\sigma}\, e^{-\frac{1}{2}[(x-\mu)/\sigma]^2} dx = p$$

or
$$\int_{-\infty}^{(L-\mu)/\sigma} \frac{e^{-t^2/2}}{\sqrt{2\pi}}\, dt + \int_{\frac{U-\mu}{\sigma}}^{\infty} \frac{e^{-t^2/2}}{\sqrt{2\pi}}\, dt = p$$

Let
$$(L - \mu)/\sigma = -K_{p'} \quad \text{and} \quad (U - \mu)/\sigma = K_{p''}$$

Then
$$\mu = \frac{LK_{p''} + UK_{p'}}{K_{p'} + K_{p''}}$$

and
$$\sigma = \frac{U - L}{K_{p'} + K_{p''}}$$

and for a given p, we may plot μ against σ and obtain a curve of constant proportion defective.   A typical curve is given in Fig. 11.3.   Thus, the

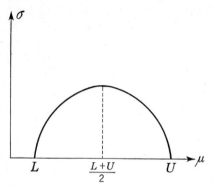

probability of acceptance given a certain fraction defective p is a function of μ and σ (or of $K_{p'}$ and $K_{p''}$) and not of p alone.

For unknown standard deviation plans, it is difficult to devise acceptance sampling procedures; in fact at present writing it is not known whether an optimum test procedure exists, although one which is good enough for practical work is derived below.

FIG. 11.3.   Curve of constant proportion defective.

One possibility is the use of two one-sided regions, that is, accept if the sample mean and sample standard deviation ($\bar{x}$ and s) lie inside a given triangle; that is, if both $\bar{x} + ks \leq U$ and $\bar{x} - ks \geq L$ are satisfied. If we let p' be the proportion defective below L and p'' be the proportion defective above U, the probability of acceptance is $L_p = L_U + L_L$, where

$$L_U = \int_{\frac{\sqrt{n}}{2}(K_{p''}-K_{p'})}^{\sqrt{n}K_{p''}} \frac{e^{-t^2/2}}{\sqrt{2\pi}} \left[\int_0^{\frac{n-1}{2k^2}\left(K_{p''}-\frac{t}{\sqrt{n}}\right)^2} \frac{y^{\frac{k-3}{2}}e^{-y}}{\left(\frac{n-3}{2}\right)!} \, dy \right] dt$$

and $$L_L = \int_{-\sqrt{n}K_{p'}}^{\frac{\sqrt{n}}{2}(K_{p''}-K_{p'})} \frac{e^{-t^2/2}}{\sqrt{2\pi}} \left[\int_0^{\frac{n-1}{2k^2}\left(K_{p'}+\frac{t}{\sqrt{n}}\right)^2} \frac{y^{(n-3)/2}e^{-y}}{\left(\frac{n-3}{2}\right)!} \, dy \right] dt$$

Unfortunately L_p does not depend just on p but on both p' and p''. It can be shown by elementary methods that L_p is a maximum for $p' = p'' = p/2$ and a minimum for $p' = p$, $p'' = 0$ or $p'' = p$, $p' = 0$. For $p'' = p$, $p' = 0$, L_p is just equal to the OC curve of the one-sided test based on k; that is, $L_p = P(\bar{x} + ks \leq U)$.   Thus no matter how p is divided, L_p exceeds or equals the OC curve of the one-sided test and attains its maximum value for $p' = p'' = p/2$.

Thus, no matter how the proportion defective is divided between the limits, the OC curve will be between two bounds.   The lower bound will be the OC curve of the one-sided plan on which the two-sided plan is based.   This curve describes the operation of the pair of criteria for the limiting case in which the defectives are not divided outside of the limits but all lie beyond only one of the limits. The upper bound for the OC curve will be the probability of accepting in the other limiting case, the case in which the defectives are equally divided beyond the two specification limits. The actual OC curve for the lots to which the criteria are applied will lie on or somewhere between these two bounds. Its actual position will depend on the way the defectives are divided between items with measurements that are too large and items with measurements that are too small. However, one may be sure that no matter what division actually occurs, the realized curve will lie between these known bounds.

For some plans the two bounds will lie close together so that the actual division of defectives between the limits makes little difference. Under other plans the bounds are a relatively great distance apart so that the way the defectives are distributed will have considerable influence on the risks of acceptance and rejection. For low AQL classes and small sample-size letters, there is little difference in the ability of the pair of criteria to discriminate, regardless of the way the proportion defective is divided between the specification limits. An indication of how the operating characteristics are affected by the division of the percentage defective for the range of sample sizes and the range of AQL classes is given by Table 11.1. This table shows for representative sample-size

TABLE 11.1. EXACT PROBABILITIES FOR TWO-SIDED TESTING USING SINGLE-LIMIT CONSTANTS WHEN PROPORTION DEFECTIVE IS EQUALLY DIVIDED

Sample-size letter	AQL class	Probability for two-sided test	
		At single-limit AQL (Standard probability: 0.95)	At single-limit LTPD (Standard probability: 0.10)
C	0.65 –1.2	0.9683	0.1481
	3.2 –4.4	0.9794	0.1985
	6.4 –8.5	0.9902	0.3205
F	0.17 –0.22	0.9695	0.1537
	1.2 –2.2	0.9857	0.2487
	5.3 –6.4	0.9943	0.3933
J	0.06 –0.12	0.9836	0.2267
	1.2 –2.2	0.9967	0.4578
	5.3 –6.4	0.9995	0.7183
M	0.035–0.06	0.9871	0.2680
	0.22 –0.32	0.9937	0.3594
	2.2 –3.2	0.9994	0.6795

letters and representative AQL classes the exact probabilities of acceptance for percentages defective at the AQL and LTPD points for the two-sided test when there is an even division of the proportion defective. The probabilities in the first column are to be compared to the value 0.95, and the probabilities in the second column to the value 0.10, which are the standard probabilities of acceptance at the AQL and at the LTPD, respectively. This comparison will indicate the extent to which the upper and lower bounds for the OC curve will differ.

From these illustrations it is apparent that for the larger AQL classes and the larger sample-size letters the way in which the proportion defective is divided will make considerable difference in the realized operating characteristics of a pair of criteria. If, for example, a plan is selected on the basis of the single-limit OC curve or AQL and LTPD values, and the defectives in submitted lots happen to be fairly evenly divided, the actual protection against the acceptance of bad lots will be much less than the protection anticipated. Clearly the upper and lower bounds do not define the risk of acceptance with sufficient accuracy for practical application, and another solution to the problem had to be found.

Actually, before considering the test procedures, it is informative to consider the related problem of estimating the proportion of a normal distribution outside two given limits. Actually all variables inspection procedures for percent defective may be interpreted as follows: calculate an estimate $\hat{p}$ of the proportion defective p from the variables data; reject if $\hat{p}$ exceeds some critical value; accept if it is small. Two solutions to this problem which seem reasonable intuitively have been proposed, one by Arnold[†] and one by Wolfowitz.[‡] Both use the estimate

$$\hat{p} = 1 - \frac{1}{\sqrt{2\pi}} \int_{(L-\bar{x})/s}^{(U-\bar{x})/s} e^{-t^2/2} \, dt$$

but differ in their approximations to the distribution of $\hat{p}$; Wolfowitz essentially considers only the sampling variation in s and shows that his procedure is asymptotically correct. It will in general be a good approximation for large σ. Arnold uses the non-central t distribution which will probably be a good approximation for small σ. However, an estimate of $\hat{p}$ which seems preferable to the preceding ones is the conditional expected value of the observed proportion defective outside L

† See Statistical Research Group, Columbia University, "Techniques of Statistical Analysis," Chap. 1, Sec. 10.2, McGraw-Hill Book Company, Inc., New York, 1947.

‡ Wolfowitz, J., "Confidence Limits for the Fraction of a Normal Population Which Lies between Two Given Limits," *The Annals of Mathematical Statistics*, Vol. 17, No. 4, December, 1946.

and U given $\bar{x}$ and s. It follows from work of Blackwell† that this statistic is the best (in the sense of minimum variance) unbiased estimate of p. The expression for this estimate is

$$\hat{p} = \int_0^{\max\left[0,\frac{1}{2}-\frac{\sqrt{N}}{2}\frac{U-\bar{x}}{s(N-1)}\right]} \frac{t^{N/2-2}(1-t)^{N/2-1}\,dt}{\beta(N/2-1,\,N/2-1)}$$

$$+ \int_0^{\max\left[0,\frac{1}{2}-\frac{\sqrt{N}}{2}\frac{\bar{x}-L}{s(N-1)}\right]} \frac{t^{N/2-2}(1-t)^{N/2-1}\,dt}{\beta(N/2-1,\,N/2-1)}$$

The test procedure we are interested in developing is of the following sort: Accept if $\hat{p} < p^*$, where p^* is a suitably chosen constant; reject otherwise.

If this test procedure is to be satisfactory it should give approximately the same OC curve for all values of μ and σ for a constant p, and in particular when all the p is on one side (say above U), the test should have the OC curve of a one-sided test. In this case the estimate of p is

$$\hat{p} = \int_0^{\max\left[0,\frac{1}{2}-\frac{\sqrt{N}}{2}\frac{U-\bar{x}}{s(N-1)}\right]} d\beta\left(\frac{N}{2}-1,\frac{N}{2}-1\right)$$

and the rule accept if $\hat{p} < p^*$ is equivalent to accept if

$$\frac{1}{2} - \frac{\sqrt{N}}{2}\frac{U-\bar{x}}{s(N-1)} < \beta_p{}^*$$

where $\beta_p{}^*$ is defined by

$$\int_0^{\beta_p{}^*} d\beta\left(\frac{N}{2}-1,\frac{N}{2}-1\right) = p^*$$

To choose p^* so that for a given N and p_0 the OC curve will be $1-\alpha$, we take p^* such that

$$P\left\{\frac{1}{2} - \frac{\sqrt{N}}{2}\frac{U-\bar{x}}{N-1} < \beta_p{}^* \,\middle|\, \mu,\sigma,p_0\right\} = 1-\alpha$$

which leads to

$$\beta_p{}^* = \frac{1}{2} - \frac{t_0(N-1,\,\sqrt{N}kp_0,\,1-\alpha)}{2(N-1)}$$

where t_0 is the value of non-central t with $N-1$ degrees of freedom, exceeded with probability $1-\alpha$.

† Blackwell, David, "Conditional Expectation and Unbiased Sequential Estimation," *The Annals of Mathematical Statistics*, Vol. 18, No. 1, March, 1947.

We propose to use this p^* with the two-sided region. Unfortunately, the OC curve of the region does not depend only on p; however, it is close enough to the one-sided OC curve for all practical purposes. A number of cases for various divisions of p are presented in Table 11.2.

TABLE 11.2. EXAMPLES OF MATCH BETWEEN ONE-SIDED AND TWO-SIDED TESTING
    FOR VARIOUS DIVISIONS OF THE PROPORTION DEFECTIVE, $N = 50$

p	p'	p''	Two-sided OC curve	One-sided OC curve
.0100	.0050	.0050	.9721	
.0100	.0030	.0070	.9721	.9743
.0152	.0076	.0076	.8959	
.0152	.0052	.0100	.8959	.9000
.0236	.0118	.0118	.6989	
.0236	.0036	.0200	.6991	.7000
.0315	.01575	.01575	.5014	
.0315	.0050	.0265	.5013	.5000
.0592	.0296	.0296	.1066	
.0592	.0150	.0442	.1065	.1000

To summarize, there are three arguments for using this principle of testing (that is, basing the decision on the conditional expected proportion of defectives given $\bar{x}$ and s):

1. This is an optimum solution to the related estimation problem; that is, this estimate of p has minimum variance.

2. This principle gives the one-sided test which has other optimum properties.

3. The OC curve is for all practical purposes just a function of p.

It remains to devise procedures for the construction of the regions.

Now $\hat{p}$ consists of two components, or one, or none, depending on the relation of $\bar{x}$ and s to U and L.

If $\dfrac{U - \bar{x}}{s[(N - 1)/\sqrt{N}]} > 1$, or if $\bar{x} < U - s[(N - 1)/\sqrt{N}]$, there is no contribution from above. Similarly if $\bar{x} > L + s[(N - 1)/\sqrt{N}]$, there is no contribution from below.

If $U - s[(N - 1)/\sqrt{N}] < \bar{x} < L + s[(N - 1)/\sqrt{N}]$, both sides contribute. Write

$$p' = \int_0^{\frac{1}{2} - \frac{1}{2}\frac{U - \bar{x}}{s[(N-1)/\sqrt{N}]}} d\beta \qquad \text{and} \qquad p'' = \int_0^{\frac{1}{2} - \frac{\sqrt{N}}{2}\frac{\bar{x} - L}{s(N-1)}} d\beta$$

in this case. Then $\hat{p} = p' + p''$. Clearly we are at the boundary of the region $\hat{p} \leq p^*$ if

$$\beta_{p'} = \frac{1}{2} - \frac{1}{2} \frac{U - \bar{x}}{s[(N - 1)/\sqrt{N}]}$$

and

$$\beta_{p''} = \frac{1}{2} - \frac{1}{2} \frac{\bar{x} - L}{s[(N - 1)/\sqrt{N}]}$$

where $p' + p'' = p^*$. The solution for these equations for $\bar{x}$ and s is

$$s = \frac{U - L}{2[(N - 1)/\sqrt{N}](1 - \beta_{p'} - \beta_{p''})}$$

and

$$\bar{x} = \frac{U(1 - 2\beta_{p''}) - L(2\beta_{p'} - 1)}{2 - 2\beta_{p'} - 2\beta_{p''}}$$

If we let $U = 1$ and $L = -1$, then

$$s = \frac{\sqrt{N}}{(N - 1)(1 - \beta_{p'} - \beta_{p''})}$$

and

$$\bar{x} = \frac{\beta_{p'} - \beta_{p''}}{1 - \beta_{p'} - \beta_{p''}}$$

To construct the region when

$$U - s\left[\frac{(N - 1)}{\sqrt{N}}\right] < \bar{x} < L + s\left[\frac{(N - 1)}{\sqrt{N}}\right]$$

and $U = 1, L = -1$, divide the given p into two parts p' and p'' such that $p' + p'' = p^*$, and find the corresponding $\bar{x}$, s on the boundary. The value of β_x is that value of the variable in a beta distribution with parameters $N/2 - 1$, $N/2 - 1$, below which x proportion of the density lies.

Thus the acceptance region corresponding to $\hat{p} \leq p^*$ is bounded by the straight line $\bar{x} = L + (1 - 2\beta_p{}^*)s[(N - 1)/\sqrt{N}]$ for $L < \bar{x} < L + \delta$; by the straight line $\bar{x} = U(1 - 2\beta_p{}^*)s[(N - 1)/\sqrt{N}]$ for $U - \delta < \bar{x} < U$; and by the curve that is determined from the p', p'' divisions for $L + \delta < \bar{x} < U - \delta$.

We may determine $\pm\delta$, the values of $\bar{x}$ at which the curved portion of the boundary intersects the straight-line portions, by eliminating s from

$$\begin{cases} \bar{x} = L + (1 - 2\beta_p{}^*)s\dfrac{N - 1}{\sqrt{N}} \\ \bar{x} = U - s\dfrac{N - 1}{\sqrt{N}} \end{cases}$$

whence

$$\bar{x} = U - \frac{1 - 2\beta_p{}^*}{1 - \beta_p{}^*}$$

If we let $U = 1$,

$$\delta = \frac{\beta_p{}^*}{1 - \beta_p{}^*}$$

4. COMBINED VARIABLES AND ATTRIBUTE PLANS

In Sec. 12 of Chap. 5 we have indicated the advantages in the use of a procedure combining variables and attribute sampling inspection plans. A general procedure for a combined plan is as follows: A sample of size m_1 is taken and subjected to the variables criterion $\bar{x} + ks \leq U$. If the inequality is satisfied, the lot is accepted. If $\bar{x} + ks > U$, a second sample of size m_2 is drawn. If the number of defectives in the $m_1 + m_2$ items is less than or equal to the acceptance number a, the lot is accepted; if not, the lot is rejected. Since the combined data is subjected to the attribute test, the first and second sample results are not independent. The exact OC curve for the procedure outlined above is therefore difficult to obtain. Instead of the curve, we shall indicate bounds for it which are reasonably close in most cases.

Let A be the condition that $\bar{x} + ks \leq U$, R be the condition that $\bar{x} + ks > U$, and B the condition that the number of defectives in both samples be less than a. Then the probability L_p of accepting a lot characterized by proportion defective p is given by $L_p = P(A) + P(RB)$. $P(A)$ is obtainable exactly by use of the Johnson and Welch tables, and bounds on $P(RB)$ are obtained as follows: Let d_2 denote the number of defectives in the second sample of m_2 items and d the number of defectives in the combined sample. Then if B denotes the condition that $d \leq a$ and B_2 the condition that $d_2 \leq a$, it is clear that $B \subset B_2$ and therefore $P(RB) < P(RB_2) = P(R)P(B_2)$. Since B_2 refers to the second sample only and R to the first sample only, $P(R)$ and $P(B_2)$ are independent. Also $P(RB) \leq P(B)$. We have in general that

$$P(X + Y) = P(X) + P(Y) - P(XY) \leq 1$$

Therefore $P(RB) \leq \max\ [0, P(R) + P(B) - 1]$ and hence for bounds on $P(RB)$ we have

$$\max\ [0, P(R) + P(B) - 1] \leq P(RB) \leq \min\ [P(B), P(R)P(B_2)]$$

$P(R)$ may be evaluated by using the Johnson and Welch tables, and $P(B)$ is given exactly by the sum of the first $a + 1$ terms in the binomial expansion $[p + (1 - p)]^{m_1+m_2}$; that is,

$$P(B) = \sum_{r=0}^{a} {}_{m_1+m_2}C_r p^r q^{m_1+m_2-r}$$

In the text, a simplified procedure for the combined plan is described. One of the standard single-sampling variables plans is used for the first sample variables analysis. If the lot is not accepted, that is, if $\bar{x} + ks \leq U$ is not satisfied, a second sample of size $3n/2$ is drawn and an attribute analysis with acceptance number zero is made using only the items in the second sample. The OC curve L_p for this procedure is given simply and exactly, since the two samples are treated independently. In this case, $L_p = P(A) + P(R)P(B_2)$; $P(A)$ and $P(R) = 1 - P(A)$ are given by an entry in the Johnson and Welch tables and

$$P(B_2) = (1 - p)^{3n/2}$$

Actually since a standard plan is used for the first sample, $P(A)$ and $P(R)$ may be read directly from the OC curve for the chosen plan as given in Table E.]

APPENDIX

COMPUTING TECHNIQUES AND METHODS OF APPLYING THE ACCEPTANCE CRITERIA

1. COMPUTATION OF Σx AND Σx^2

Regardless of the choice of method of applying the acceptance criterion to the sample data, the first requirement is to calculate the sum and the sum of the squares of the measurements for the sample items. For example, to use the criterion in the form $\bar{x} + ks \leq U$, where $\bar{x}$ and s must be calculated explicitly, the two sums Σx and Σx^2 are needed for the formulas $\bar{x} = \Sigma x/n$ and $s = \sqrt{[n \Sigma x^2 - (\Sigma x)^2]/[(n)(n-1)]}$. The same sums appear in any other formulation of the acceptance criterion.

The most obvious and straightforward computation method is first to write down in a column the observed value for each item in the sample as it is inspected and then to square each observation value, placing the squared values in a second column. The square of each value can be easily obtained from a standard table of squares if there are four or less digits in the recorded measurements or can be obtained by multiplication, either mentally or by machine. Adding to obtain Σx and Σx^2 is then a separate operation which can be performed either with or without the aid of a machine.

Writing down and adding the column of squares can be eliminated by the use of a calculating machine which performs accumulative multiplication. As each successive value is multiplied by itself, the sum of the squares accumulates in the "product" dial while the sum of the measurements accumulates in the "counting" dial, providing both Σx and Σx^2 directly and in one operation. This accumulative method enables a computer to make the required calculations quickly and efficiently even for large sample sizes and for measurements with a relatively large number of digits and so is recommended for use in most situations.

One simplification which can be applied to any procedure for computing Σx and Σx^2 is to reduce the number of digits in the recorded measurements to the justifiable minimum. If there are one or more digits at the left, which always appear in each measurement, these digits can be dropped in recording the measurements and therefore eliminated from all succeeding calculations. If this is done, the specification limit is adjusted accordingly for the acceptance procedure by dropping the same digits.

For example, suppose the upper limit for a dimension measurement is specified as 1.364 inches and the measurements are recorded to the nearest 0.001 inch and will in general not vary outside the range 1.350 to 1.370. For computing, only the last two digits of each measurement need be recorded and used; that is, "1.361, 1.358, 1.362," etc., could be taken as "61, 58, 62," etc.; the specification limit would be taken as "64" in the acceptance criterion.

To reduce the number of figures in the squares and in the sums a further translation may be worth while in some situations. For the above measurements, for example, it might be practical to take 1.350 as a base and either to set the measuring device to read zero at 1.350 inches or to record the measurements in terms of this number as a base for acceptance sampling procedures. If this were done, the above-measured values would be taken and used as "11, 8, 12," etc.; the specification limit would be "14."

Another possibility to reduce the number of figures is to take and use measurements in terms of the specification limit set equal to zero as a base. Under this possibility either the measuring device may be set so as to measure for each item the deviations from the specification limit or absolute measurements may be taken and converted into deviations from the limit. Thus in the example above the values recorded and used would be "3, 6, 2," etc., and the specification limit would be "0." This last type of translation necessitates changing the sign of the mean of the values in the acceptance criterion when the specification is an upper limit. The occasional values that may be found outside the limit must, of course, be handled as negative numbers. Simplified methods of applying the acceptance criteria to data in this form are discussed in detail later in this Appendix.

A practical way in many situations of reducing the time and effort required for recording data and making the computations is to tally the observations, that is, to collect identical measured values or values falling within assigned ranges instead of writing and using each observation individually. The advantage of the tally method lies mainly in the elimination of repeated squaring of the same numbers. The importance of this advantage will be greater for large samples and for coarsely grouped data. This latter situation is illustrated in Table A.1 which contains a tally of the Rockwell hardness test data for the sample of 25 sheets of metal as given in Table 8.1. Another advantage of the tally method is that, if the product contains an unusual pattern of quality, such as a truncated or abnormally skewed distribution to which the variables plans should not be applied, this fact may be discovered by observation of a series of tallies. Another possible advantage is that the crude graphical picture of the frequency distribution thus obtained may be an aid in convincing the supplier of the necessity of rejection and may help him in detecting certain kinds of production difficulties.

The inspection supervisor must realize that tallying the measurements as they are obtained may lead to some personal bias on the part of the inspector. For example, for items whose measurement falls slightly outside the limit, he may tend to give the product the benefit of the doubt and tally such measurements under the number or cell just at the specification limit, particularly if the value for the specification limit is marked on the sheet beforehand. He may also unconsciously be influenced to throw borderline measurements between cell boundaries into the cells which, either by pure chance or because of the nature of the distribution of item measurements, seem to be lagging in the tally race at the time.

In situations where it is meaningful to retain the order in which items are inspected, the tally method may be undesirable. This might be true, for example, if order of inspection is related to order of production or if

TABLE A.1. ROCKWELL HARDNESS, B SCALE
(x = hardness number)

x	f	fx	fx^2
66	1	66	4,356
65	2	130	8,450
64	2	128	8,192
63			
62	3	186	11,532
61	5	305	18,605
60	4	240	14,400
59	4	236	13,924
58			
57	3	171	9,747
56	1	56	3,136
	25	1518	92,342
	(n)	(Σx)	(Σx^2)

proportional sampling of the lots is practiced. However, order of inspection can be retained if items are tallied by recording sequence identification numbers on the tally sheet instead of the usual tally marks. Thus one cell may receive the numbers 3, 12, 16, indicating that the third, twelfth, and sixteenth items inspected were of that magnitude. In the case of proportional sampling, identity of items can be maintained by using different colors or different types of tally marks. Identification of measured values with particular items or sample subgroups simplifies rechecking of doubtful measurements and preserves information that may be of considerable value in detecting and segregating nonconforming material.

Ordinarily the observed values will be rounded off, either in the measuring procedure or at the time of recording each measurement, and in most cases will be grouped into a reasonable number of class intervals. The Rockwell hardness data shown in Table A.1, for example, was grouped by the limitations of the particular measurement scale into 11 cells or class intervals. Rounding off observed values saves computation time in that there are fewer digits and permits greater use of the tally method. For instance, the thickness measurements of the sheets of metal as given in Table 8.1 have been rounded to the nearest 0.001 inch, giving a grouping of 24 cells. If these measurements had been recorded to the nearest 0.0001 inch, there would be 240 natural groupings. Obviously rounding off or grouping of measured values to reduce calculation time discards some of the available information and therefore reduces to some extent the reliability of the sampling test. A good general rule is to have the class intervals less than one-third and preferably less than one-fourth of the lot standard deviation.† Decisions concerning the grouping of data should be made with the realization that the cost of calculations is only one of the more obvious costs affected. In some cases where variables sampling plans are most useful, the relatively high costs of item inspection will warrant retaining throughout the calculations the full degree of precision of measurements that is available so that a maximum amount of information may be obtained from a small sample. However in a majority of situations little reliability of the sampling test is lost by rounding off or grouping as long as 10 or more class intervals are retained.

2. THE STANDARD METHOD

The standard method of applying the acceptance criterion is the straightforward use of the criterion in the form $\bar{x} + ks \leq U$ (or $\bar{x} - ks \geq L$). The steps for this method of application are:

(1) Compute Σx and Σx^2.

(2) Using Σx and Σx^2, compute the sample mean $\bar{x}$ and the sample standard deviation s.

(3) Using the appropriate value for k, compute $\bar{x} + ks$ (or $\bar{x} - ks$) and compare with the upper (or lower) specification limit. The sample mean is computed by the formula $\bar{x} = \Sigma x/n$. As indicated, the sum of the n different values of x may be divided by n to obtain $\bar{x}$. However,

---

† For a complete discussion see Statistical Research Group, Columbia University, "Techniques of Statistical Analysis," Chap. 4, McGraw-Hill Book Company, Inc., New York, 1947.

TABLE A.2.   FACTORS TO SIMPLIFY THE COMPUTATION OF $\bar{x}$ AND s

n	$\dfrac{1}{n}$	$\dfrac{1}{n(n-1)}$
3	0.3333	0.1667
4	0.2500	0.08333
5	0.2000	0.05000
6	0.1667	0.03333
7	0.1429	0.02381
8	0.1250	0.01786
9	0.1111	0.01389
10	0.1000	0.01111
11	0.09091	0.009091
12	0.08333	0.007576
13	0.07692	0.006410
14	0.07143	0.005495
15	0.06667	0.004762
16	0.06250	0.004167
18	0.05556	0.003268
20	0.05000	0.002632
22	0.04545	0.002165
24	0.04167	0.001812
25	0.04000	0.001667
28	0.03571	0.001323
30	0.03333	0.001149
32	0.03125	0.001008
35	0.02857	0.0008403
36	0.02778	0.0007937
40	0.02500	0.0006410
45	0.02222	0.0005051
50	0.02000	0.0004082
55	0.01818	0.0003367
60	0.01667	0.0002825
70	0.01429	0.0002070
85	0.01176	0.0001401
100	0.01000	0.0001010
125	0.008000	0.00006452
200	0.005000	0.00002513

if a calculating machine is used, it is generally quicker to multiply Σx by $1/n$; values of $1/n$ are given in Table A.2, page 147.

The sample standard deviation should always be computed by the formula

$$s = \sqrt{\frac{n\,\Sigma x^2 - (\Sigma x)^2}{n(n-1)}}$$

The value under the radical (s^2) can be easily obtained on a calculating machine as follows:

(1) Multiply Σx^2 by n.

(2) Using (negative) cumulative multiplication, subtract $(\Sigma x)(\Sigma x)$.

(3) Divide the result of (2) by $n(n-1)$ or multiply result of (2) by $1/(n)(n-1)$ obtained from Table A.2.

Extraction of the square root of the value obtained in (3) to get s may be accomplished by slide rule or by inverse use of a standard table of squares.   If more accuracy is required, a fairly rapid and efficient method of obtaining square roots on a calculator can be found in manuals published by the machine manufacturers.   The sum $\bar{x} + ks$ (or $\bar{x} - ks$) may be computed on the calculating machine without writing down the value of ks, by means of the cumulative multiplication technique.

3. INSPECTION AND COMPUTATION FORMS

A standard form may be used to advantage, particularly if the calculations must be made by hand or by a person of limited experience with a calculator.   The form in Fig. A.1, for example, was designed to serve as both an inspection record and calculation sheet for the application of single-sample acceptance criteria by the standard method.

In practice, the values of k, n, $1/n$, $1/(n)(n-1)$, and U (or L) and the data in the heading of the sheet are all entered in advance from the lot order and the inspector's instruction or specification sheet.   The use of such a form will tend to minimize computational mistakes, will aid standardization of the procedures, and will preserve the inspection results for all lots in common arrangement.   In some situations a computing form may also effect a noticeable saving of time and effort.

4. AN OPTIONAL FORM FOR THE STANDARD CRITERIA

It seems most straightforward and perhaps most useful for the criteria under variables inspection to be in the form as used throughout the text and as used above in Sec. 2 of the Appendix, but there are many alternative methods.   In the standard form certain calculations are made, using a constant from the sampling plan and the resulting value compared with the specification limit for the item.   An alternative form may be used in which the computations involve the specification limit and the resulting value is compared with the constant from the sampling plan.   To some

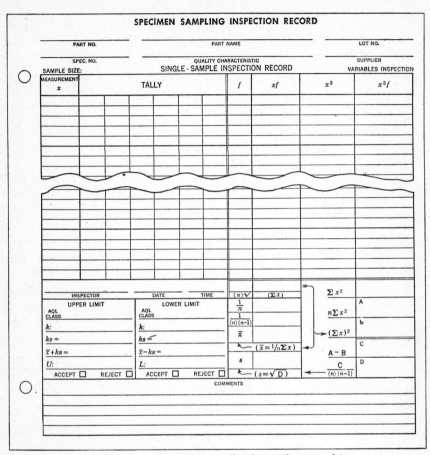

Fig. A.1.   Specimen sampling inspection record.

this method may seem preferable.   The criteria may be reexpressed in this optional form as follows:

a. Single Sampling.   With U an upper limit, accept the lot if

$$\frac{U - \bar{x}}{s} \geq k \tag{63}$$

With L a lower limit, accept the lot if

$$\frac{\bar{x} - L}{s} \geq k \tag{64}$$

b. Double Sampling

1. *Criteria for the first sample.* With U an upper limit, accept the lot if

$$\frac{U - \bar{x}_1}{s_1} \geq k_a \tag{65}$$

With L a lower limit, accept the lot if

$$\frac{\bar{x}_1 - L}{s_1} \geq k_a \tag{66}$$

With U an upper limit, reject the lot if

$$\frac{U - \bar{x}_1}{s_1} \leq k_r \tag{67}$$

With L a lower limit, reject the lot if

$$\frac{\bar{x}_1 - L}{s_1} \leq k_r \tag{68}$$

2. *Criteria for the second sample.* With U an upper limit, accept the lot if

$$\frac{U - \bar{x}_t}{s_t} \geq k_t \tag{69}$$

With L a lower limit, accept the lot if

$$\frac{\bar{x}_t - L}{s_t} \geq k_t \tag{70}$$

All suggestions regarding the computing techniques with the use of the standard form of the criteria apply also to this alternative form.

5. THE DIFFERENCE METHOD

As indicated earlier in the Appendix, the computations are simplified if the data and the specification limit are adjusted to reduce the number of digits handled. One method of adjustment mentioned is to choose the specification limit as a reference point, assigning to it the value zero, and to measure items in terms of the difference y between the specification limit (U or L) and the value of x or to convert absolute measurements into these terms. Then, by definition,

$$y = U - x \tag{71}$$

if the specification is an upper limit, or

$$y = x - L \tag{72}$$

if the specification is a lower limit.   In either case, y is taken in a positive sense, and it can be shown algebraically that the acceptance criterion becomes

$$\bar{y} \geq ks \tag{73}$$

The sample standard deviation s is computed by the formula

$$s = \sqrt{\frac{n\Sigma y^2 - (\Sigma y)^2}{(n)(n-1)}} \tag{74}$$

and will be the same as if Σx and Σx^2 were used, provided that both the original and transformed data are given in the same decimal units.   If, however, the original data is transformed by one of the following equations: $y = a(U - x)$ or $y = a(x - L)$, where, for example, a equals 100 or 0.001, then the standard deviation for the transformed data is a times the standard deviation for the original data.

The difference method is essentially a modification of the standard method for use where the difference between the specification limit and the value of the quality characteristic can be readily obtained.   The first two steps in this application of the difference method are identical with those given under the standard method except that the transformed data is used.   The third step is the comparison $\bar{y}$ with ks, where s refers to the standard deviation for the transformed data.   The acceptance criterion for both an upper and lower specification limit is

$$\bar{y} \geq ks \tag{73}$$

6. THE QUADRATIC METHOD—ANALYTICAL SOLUTION

It is possible to set up a procedure using calculations in which $\bar{x}$, the sample mean, and s, the sample standard deviation, need not be determined explicitly.   The test criterion $\bar{x} + ks \leq U$ or $\bar{x} - ks \geq L$ can be expressed in terms of the sum of the item measurements Σx and the sum of the measurements squared Σx^2.

For single sampling, the required steps with their formulas are as follows:

(a) Obtain the sum Σx and the sum of the squares Σx^2 of the measurements.

(b) Apply a first acceptance criterion.   Under this method the data is submitted to a first acceptance criterion of the form

$$\Sigma x^2 \leq k_w U^2 \tag{75}$$

or

$$\Sigma x^2 \geq k_w L^2 \tag{76}$$

where

$$k_w = \frac{n-1}{k^2+1} \tag{77}$$

This is a criterion of a very simple form which will accept without further calculations lots that are much better than expected. Values of k_w for each of the variables plans are given in Table F. The value of $k_w U^2$ or $k_w L^2$ when once calculated for the product tolerance limit and the sampling plan in use is available for each succeeding lot.

If this first acceptance criterion is met by each measured property, the lot may be accepted without further calculations. If the lot is not accepted by this criterion, the data is submitted to a second acceptance criterion which will determine the proper disposal of the lot.

(c) Apply a second acceptance criterion. Restatement of the standard acceptance criteria in terms of Σx and Σx^2 so as to eliminate the necessity of computing $\bar{x}$ and s explicitly yields the following quadratic expressions:

$$\Sigma x^2 \leq k_x(\Sigma x)^2 - k_y U(\Sigma x) + k_z U^2 \tag{78}$$

and
$$\Sigma x^2 \leq k_x(\Sigma x)^2 - k_y L(\Sigma x) + k_z L^2 \tag{79}$$

where
$$k_x = \frac{nk^2 + n - 1}{n^2 k^2} \tag{80}$$

$$k_y = \frac{2(n-1)}{nk^2} \tag{81}$$

and
$$k_z = \frac{n-1}{k^2} \tag{82}$$

If this criterion is satisfied, the lot is accepted; if it is not satisfied, the lot is rejected. The values of k_x, k_y, and k_z for each of the variables plans are given in Table F.

Where lots of a given product occur frequently, it may be worth while to simplify the criterion for each specification limit to the form

$$\Sigma x^2 \leq a(\Sigma x)^2 - b(\Sigma x) + c \tag{83}$$

where
$$a = k_x \tag{84}$$
$$b = k_y U \text{ or } k_y L \tag{85}$$

and
$$c = k_z U^2 \text{ or } k_z L^2 \tag{86}$$

If this is done, the constants a, b, and c may be computed once and retained for use with all lots rather than being recomputed each time.

The quadratic method calls for some calculations to be made prior to starting operations under the selected plan, but once this is done, the routine calculations for each lot under actual operation of the plan will be somewhat simpler than under plans calling for the calculation of $\bar{x}$ and s. In particular, the method requires fewer multiplications and additions, requires no dividing, and eliminates the necessity of taking square roots. The calculations for this procedure may be arranged on a form just as easily as those for the standard method. Hence, use of this optional form of the criteria may be quite desirable when a considerable number of lots are to be inspected under a plan.   The major disadvantage of this method is the difficulty of interpretation of the quantities Σx^2 and $a(\Sigma x)^2 - b\Sigma x + c$ and of the margin by which acceptance or rejection is indicated.   Of course, inspection decisions in borderline cases may be easier for the inspector if the figures he uses are of obscure significance to him.   However, for the same reason, mistakes in inspection and computing may be more likely to pass undetected.

7. THE QUADRATIC METHOD—GRAPHICAL SOLUTION

For each of the methods of applying the criteria there is a possibility of eliminating one or more computational steps by the use of a graphical solution.   In most situations the graphical method is not likely to be advantageous when the acceptance criterion is used in its standard form or in one of its variations in which the mean and the standard deviation must be calculated, particularly where only a single limit exists.   For the standard form, for example, the only steps eliminated by the graphical solution are the multiplication by k and the addition of $\bar{x}$ and ks (or the subtraction of ks from $\bar{x}$).   However, when the quadratic form of the criterion is used, a graphical solution possesses the advantage of eliminating in the routine operation of the plan all the relatively numerous computational steps beyond the basic computations of Σx and Σx^2.   Some initial time and effort for computing and drawing the graph is required prior to the start of operation, but when a large number of lots are to be sampled, this may be quickly repaid by the savings in computation time.

For single sampling and for the case where a one-sided limit is specified, the steps in a graphical solution are as follows:

(a) Prepare a graph of the quadratic form of the test criterion.   This step is performed, presumably by the inspection supervisor, prior to operations under the plan.   The appropriate inequality as shown in formulas (78) and (79) or the inequality as shown by formula (83) is used, and values for k_x, k_y, and k_z as determined by the selected plan and the specified specification limit are inserted.   The inequality is then plotted on graph paper, Σx horizontally and Σx^2 vertically, using the equality sign.   The parabola thus obtained will represent the maximum value of Σx^2 for a given Σx which will permit the acceptance of the lot.   In addition, a so-called "error curve" may also be plotted on the same sheet.   This curve, obtained by taking the limiting case of a standard deviation of zero for the sample, is given by

$$\Sigma x^2 = \frac{(\Sigma x)^2}{n} \tag{87}$$

A value of Σx^2 for a given Σx which falls on this line would indicate a standard deviation of zero for the sample; a point falling below would indicate an error in the computations.

(b) Obtain the sum Σx and the sum of squares Σx^2 of the measurements for the sample.

(c) Plot the values for Σx and Σx^2 on the graph. If the point falls below the curve representing the quadratic equation, the lot is acceptable for the characteristic being tested; if the point falls above this curve, the lot is not acceptable. If the point falls below the error curve, indicating that an error has been made in the computations, the computations must be redone so that correct values for Σx and Σx^2 may be obtained and plotted. The use of the graph for evaluating data from successive lots may be simplified by labeling each of the areas as well as each of the curves; the area above the upper curve is labeled the "rejection region," the area between the upper curve and the error curve the "acceptance region," and the area below the error curve the "error region."

To illustrate this procedure a graph has been prepared for application to the Rockwell hardness measurements on the sheets of metal described in Sec. 1 of Chap. 8. For this product, an upper limit U of 68 for hardness numbers has been specified, the AQL class 0.65 to 1.2 percent defective has been selected, and sample-size letter G is to be used. For this sample-size letter and AQL class Table F gives values of 0.0525 for k_x, 0.623 for k_y, and 7.783 for k_z. Substitution of these values and the value for U in Eq. (78) gives

$$\Sigma x^2 = (0.0525)(\Sigma x)^2 - (42.36)(\Sigma x) + 35{,}989$$

This equation has been plotted as the upper curve in Fig. A.2. The equation for the error curve is obtained by substituting the sample size $n = 25$ in Eq. (87) giving

$$\Sigma x^2 = \frac{(\Sigma x)^2}{25}$$

The curve representing this equation has also been drawn in Fig. A.2. The sample data for one of the lots as given in Chap. 8 gives the value 1,518 for Σx and the value 92,342 for Σx^2. The point representing these values falls within the acceptance region of the graph, indicating that the lot is acceptable for this characteristic.

For item characteristics for which the measurements are large numbers, this graphical procedure may be impractical unless the observations are adjusted by the dropping of digits or the use of a provisional base as described in Sec. 1 of this Appendix. For numerically large observations, Σx^2 will be very large in comparison with Σx, and in adjusting the scales of the graph to plot data of this sort, the region of acceptance will be made extremely small.   One possibility is to take measurements in terms of the limit as a base or to translate them to these terms.   The graphical solution under this possibility will be briefly described in Sec. 9 of this Appendix.

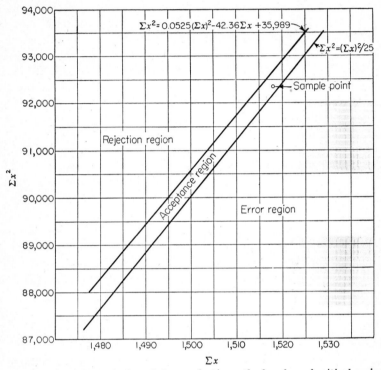

FIG. A.2.   Graphical solution of the quadratic method, enlarged critical region.

8. THE SQUARED-DIFFERENCE METHOD—ANALYTICAL SOLUTION

An appreciable simplification of the quadratic form of the acceptance criteria is possible in cases where item measurements can be taken as deviations y from the specification limit or where absolute measurements may be converted to differences between the specification limit and the measured values.   If this is done, the criterion, whether for an upper limit or a lower limit, then reduces to

$$\Sigma y^2 \leq k_x (\Sigma y)^2 \qquad (88)$$

where $y = U - x$ or $y = x - L$.

This is the simplest form for the acceptance criterion.   All that is necessary to determine the proper disposal of a lot, once Σy and Σy^2

have been obtained for the sample, is to square the quantity Σy and multiply the result by k_x, whose value may be obtained from Table F. If the product is equal to or greater than Σy^2, the lot may be accepted; if the product is less than Σy^2, it is rejected.

9. THE SQUARED-DIFFERENCE METHOD—GRAPHICAL SOLUTION

If measurements are taken in terms of y instead of x or are converted to these terms, a decision on the disposal of each lot may be obtained directly from Σy and Σy^2 by a graphical procedure. This form of solution may be desirable in some cases as a means of further simplifying the routine work of computation. For the squared-difference method the construction of a workable graph will be generally easier than under the quadratic method because the useful numerical range of Σy^2 will be considerably smaller than for Σx^2.

The equation for plotting the limit line is obtained by securing the appropriate value of k_x from Table F and substituting it in Eq. (88). The error line as described in Sec. 7 is obtained from the equation

$$\sum y^2 = \frac{(\Sigma y)^2}{n} \tag{89}$$

Operations under this method are carried out in the same manner as under the quadratic method. As samples are inspected, the values for Σy and Σy^2 are plotted on the graph; Σy is plotted horizontally and Σy^2 vertically. If the point falls above the curve, the lot is rejected; if it falls below the curve but above the error curve, the lot is accepted; if it falls below the error curve, the calculations must be redone and correct values for Σy and Σy^2 obtained.

LIST OF SYMBOLS

The prime (′) added to a symbol indicates it is related to plans and formulas used when the standard deviation of the product is known.

a k_x. A constant used in applying the acceptance criteria in the optional form of the quadratic method.

a' $2/(U - L)$. A constant used in applying two-sided plans where the standard deviation is not known.

A A factor for computing 3-sigma control limits for sample averages when the product standard deviation is known.

$\hat{A}_1$ A factor for computing 3-sigma control limits for sample averages when the mean of sample standard deviations is taken as an estimate of the product standard deviation.

AOQ Average outgoing quality.

AOQL Average outgoing-quality limit.

AQL Acceptable quality level.

ASN Average sample number.

b $k_y U$ or $k_y L$. A constant used in applying the acceptance criteria in the optional form of the quadratic method.

b' $(L + U)/(L - U)$. A constant used in applying two-sided plans where the standard deviation is not known.

$\hat{B}_1$ A factor for computing the lower 3-sigma control limit for sample standard deviations when the product standard deviation is estimated from the average of the sample standard deviations.

$\hat{B}_2$ A factor for computing the upper 3-sigma control limit for sample standard deviations when the product standard deviation is estimated from the average of the sample standard deviations.

$\hat{B}_3$ A factor for computing the lower 3-sigma control limit for sample standard deviations when the mean of sample standard deviations is taken as an estimate of the product standard deviation.

$\hat{B}_4$ A factor for computing the upper 3-sigma control limit for sample standard deviations when the mean of sample standard deviations is taken as an estimate of the product standard deviation.

c $k_z U^2$ or $k_z L^2$. A constant used in applying the acceptance criterion in the optional form of the quadratic method.

d The coefficient of displacement.

k The coefficient of the sample standard deviation in the basic acceptance criterion for single sampling.

k' The coefficient of the population standard deviation (σ) in the basic acceptance criterion for single sampling when the standard deviation is known.

k_a The coefficient of s_1 in the first-sample acceptance criterion for double sampling.

k'_a The coefficient of σ in the first-sample acceptance criterion for double sampling for use when the standard deviation is known.

k_r The coefficient of s_1 in the first-sample rejection criterion for double sampling.

k'_r The coefficient of σ in the first-sample rejection criterion for double sampling for use when the standard deviation is known.

k_t The coefficient of s_2 in the second-sample acceptance criterion for double sampling.

k'_t The coefficient of σ in the second-sample acceptance criterion for double sampling for use when the standard deviation is known.

k_w The coefficient of U^2 (or L^2) in the first acceptance criterion for use with the quadratic method of application.

k'_L The constant associated with the AQL class chosen for testing at the lower limit when two-sided testing is used.

k'_U The constant associated with the AQL class chosen for testing at the upper limit when two-sided testing is used.

k_x The coefficient of $(\Sigma x)^2$ in the second acceptance criterion for use with the quadratic method of application.

k_y The coefficient of $U\Sigma x$ (or $L\Sigma x$) in the second acceptance criterion for use with the quadratic method of application.

k_z The coefficient of U^2 (or L^2) in the second acceptance criterion for use with the quadratic method of application.

k_L The coefficient of the sample standard deviation in the basic acceptance criterion when used for two-sided testing. This is the constant k corresponding to the single-limit plan chosen for testing at the lower limit.

k_U The coefficient of the sample standard deviation in the basic acceptance criterion when used for two-sided testing. This is the constant k corresponding to the single-limit plan chosen for testing at the upper limit.

$\bar{k}$ The difference between the specification limit and the mean of the sample items used in computing a process average as a multiple of the standard deviation of the sample items.

K The difference between the specification limit and the lot mean as a multiple of the lot standard deviation.

K_p A factor used in the computation of the OC curve for known-sigma plans. It is that particular value of K such that the area under the normal curve lying to the right of K_p is equal to p.

l_1 A constant used in computing control limits for the coefficient of displacement chart.

l_2 A constant used in computing control limits for the coefficient of displacement chart.

l_3 A constant used in computing control limits for the coefficient of displacement chart.

L The lower specification limit.

LCL   Lower control limit.

LTPD   Lot tolerance percent defective.

m The number of samples used in computing a process average.

μ The lot mean.

n The sample size for single sampling when the product standard deviation is not known.

n' The sample size for single sampling when the product standard deviation is known.

n_1 The number of items in the first sample of a double-sampling plan.

n_1' The number of items in the first sample of a double-sampling plan when the product standard deviation is known.

n_2 The number of items in the second sample of a double-sampling plan.

n_2' The number of items in the second sample of a double-sampling plan when the product standard deviation is known.

n_i The number of items in the ith sample.

N The total number of sample items used in computing a process average.

OC   Operating characteristics.

p The fraction defective of a lot.

$\bar{p}$ The average fraction defective; the center line for the p chart.

$P(A_1)$ The probability that a given variables test will accept lots of various qualities.

$P(A_2)$ The probability of obtaining no defects in a sample of size $3n/2$.

s The standard deviation of the measurements of items in a sample for a single-sampling plan.

s_1 The standard deviation of the measurements of items in the first sample of a double-sampling plan.

s_i The standard deviation of the measurements of items in the ith sample.

s_t The standard deviation of the measurements of items in the combined first and second samples of a double-sampling plan.

$\bar{s}$ The average of the standard deviations.

$\bar{\bar{s}}$ The standard deviation of the measurements of the items used in computing the process average; the pooled standard deviation of samples used in computing the process average.

σ The lot standard deviation.

$\sigma_{\bar{x}}$ The standard deviation of the sample mean.

σ_s The standard deviation of the sample standard deviation.

σ_d The standard deviation of the coefficient of displacement.

U The upper specification limit.

UCL   Upper control limit.

x The measurement for a sample item for a single-sampling plan.

x_1 The measurement for an item in the first sample of a double-sampling plan.

x_2 The measurement for an item in the second sample of a double-sampling plan.

$\bar{x}$ The sample mean in single sampling.

$\bar{x}_1$ The mean of the items in the first sample of a double-sampling plan.

$\bar{x}_i$ The mean of the measurements of items in the ith sample.

$\bar{x}_t$ The mean of the items in the combined first and second samples of a double-sampling plan.

$\bar{\bar{x}}$ The mean of the measurements of the items used in computing the process average.

y The difference between the measurement of a sample item and the specification limit for testing with one-sided limits.

$\bar{y}$ The average of differences between item measurements and the specification limit.

TABLES AND CHARTS

TABLE A.   SAMPLE-SIZE LETTER, BY INSPECTION LEVEL AND SIZE OF INSPECTION LOT

Size of inspection lot	Sample-size letter for inspection level		
	I	II	III
Under 25	B	B	D
25– 50	B	C	D
50– 100	C	D	F
100– 200	C	E	F
200– 300	D	F	G
300– 500	E	G	H
500– 800	G	H	I
800– 1,300	H	I	K
1,300– 3,200	H	J	K
3,200– 8,000	I	K	M
8,000– 22,000	J	L	N
22,000–110,000	K	M	N
110,000–550,000	L	N	O
550,000 and over	N	O	O
Approximate relative number of items inspected	1.0	1.5	2.0

Notes:

(1) Inspection level II will be used for most products under normal inspection. See Chap. 3, Sec. 8, and Chap. 4, Sec. 4, for further information.

(2) For reduced inspection, use a level one level lower (if such is available) than that used for normal inspection.

(3) For tightened inspection, use the same inspection level and sample-size letter as for normal inspection.

TABLE B. SUMMARY OF SINGLE-SAMPLING VARIABLES PLANS, CLASSIFIED BY ACCEPTABLE QUALITY LEVEL AND SAMPLE-SIZE LETTER

Values of k for acceptance criteria of the form $\bar{x} + ks \leq U$ or $\bar{x} - ks \geq L$

Sample-size letter	Single-sample size	Acceptable quality level class, in percent defective														
		.024–.035	.035–.06	.06–.12	.12–.17	.17–.22	.22–.32	.32–.65	.65–1.2	1.2–2.2	2.2–3.2	3.2–4.4	4.4–5.3	5.3–6.4	6.4–8.5	8.5–11.0
B*	7	→	→	→	→	→	→	1.636	1.449	1.242	1.107	1.053	0.969	0.820	0.696	0.595
C	10	→	→	→	→	→	→	1.757	1.562	1.400	1.287	1.186	0.994	0.971	0.789	0.687
D	13	→	→	→	→	→	1.957	1.764	1.583	1.472	1.371	1.189	1.132	0.978	0.926	0.772
E	16	→	→	→	→	2.116	2.018	1.822	1.694	1.437	1.378	1.217	1.180	1.059	0.906	0.815
F	20	→	→	→	2.246	2.180	2.080	1.880	1.749	1.504	1.388	1.351	1.218	1.090	0.997	0.884
G	25	→	→	2.395	2.306	2.239	2.137	1.933	1.756	1.569	1.504	1.385	1.261	1.161	1.019	0.924
H	35	→	2.653	2.480	2.389	2.319	2.234	2.031	1.811	1.672	1.552	1.390	1.284	1.196	1.068	1.004
I	50	→	2.737	2.559	2.466	2.395	2.288	2.075	1.875	1.677	1.554	1.424	1.329	1.271	1.138	1.065
J	60	2.908	2.775	2.596	2.502	2.430	2.322	2.107	1.905	1.723	1.567	1.440	1.345	1.272	1.148	1.088
K	70	2.940	2.806	2.625	2.530	2.457	2.349	2.132	1.958	1.764	1.616	1.481	1.383	1.284	1.173	1.106
L	85	2.977	2.842	2.659	2.563	2.490	2.380	2.171	1.986	1.810	1.640	1.515	1.415	1.298	←	←
M	100	3.006	2.870	2.709	2.589	2.528	2.424	2.237	2.040	1.841	1.674	1.557	←	←	←	←
N	125	3.043	2.905	2.743	2.621	2.575	2.455	2.267	2.104	1.856	←	←	←	←	←	←
O	200	3.110	2.970	2.832	2.737	2.649	2.523	2.352	2.155	←	←	←	←	←	←	←

Notes:

* Variables plans for sample-size letter A are not included because their use results in little saving over the corresponding attribute plans.

↓ Use the first sampling plan below arrow.   If sample size is larger than inspection-lot size, use 100 percent inspection or form larger inspection lots.

↑ Use the first sampling plan above arrow.

For tightened inspection use the same sample-size letter but choose a value for k from an acceptable-quality level class two classes lower than that used for normal inspection (if such a class and value of k are available).   See Chap. 5, Sec. 8, for further information.

TABLE C. SUMMARY OF DOUBLE-SAMPLING VARIABLES PLANS, CLASSIFIED BY ACCEPTABLE QUALITY LEVEL AND SAMPLE-SIZE LETTER

Sample-size letter	Sample (size First/Second)	Combined sample size (First/Second)	Constant	.024-.035	.035-.06	.06-.12	.12-.17	.17-.22	.22-.32	.32-.65	.65-1.2	1.2-2.2	2.2-3.2	3.2-4.4	4.4-5.3	5.3-6.4	6.4-8.5	8.5-11.0
B*	First 4 / Second 8	4 / 12	k_a							2.425	2.150	1.850	1.675	1.600	1.425	1.200	1.050	0.900
			k_r	→	→	→	→	→	→	1.350	1.150	1.000	0.900	0.825	0.750	0.500	0.475	0.400
			k_t							1.723	1.559	1.328	1.169	1.126	1.054	0.967	0.794	0.693
C	First 5 / Second 10	5 / 15	k_a							2.460	2.214	1.990	1.834	1.699	1.476	1.431	1.207	1.073
			k_r	→	→	→	→	→	→	1.096	0.894	0.872	0.805	0.716	0.559	0.492	0.402	0.347
			k_t							1.936	1.743	1.549	1.425	1.317	1.110	1.097	0.891	0.775
D	First 6 / Second 12	6 / 18	k_a						2.694	2.449	2.225	2.082	1.939	1.715	1.653	1.449	1.388	1.225
			k_r	→	→	→	→	→	1.266	1.082	0.939	0.857	0.816	0.592	0.551	0.420	0.408	0.367
			k_t						2.110	1.893	1.697	1.591	1.485	1.285	1.226	1.072	1.014	0.825
E	First 7 / Second 14	7 / 21	k_a					2.873	2.740	2.495	2.324	2.003	1.928	1.720	1.693	1.550	1.372	1.240
			k_r	→	→	→	→	1.455	1.361	1.209	1.096	0.888	0.794	0.737	0.718	0.605	0.472	0.348
			k_t					2.215	2.117	1.920	1.778	1.517	1.462	1.287	1.244	1.124	0.960	0.873
F	First 8 / Second 16	8 / 24	k_a				3.147	3.041	2.881	2.652	2.475	2.192	2.051	1.998	1.838	1.697	1.556	1.474
			k_r	→	→	→	1.414	1.344	1.273	1.209	0.990	0.813	0.689	0.654	0.566	0.442	0.354	0.260
			k_t				2.317	2.245	2.154	1.939	1.806	1.551	1.435	1.408	1.266	1.133	1.041	0.919
G	First 10 / Second 20	10 / 30	k_a			3.162	3.020	2.941	2.821	2.577	2.340	2.135	2.055	1.897	1.755	1.660	1.470	1.379
			k_r	→	→	1.850	1.723	1.676	1.581	1.439	1.312	1.154	1.059	0.933	0.854	0.791	0.601	0.550
			k_t			2.446	2.364	2.291	2.191	1.981	1.797	1.607	1.543	1.424	1.300	1.187	1.055	0.949
H	First 15 / Second 30	15 / 45	k_a		3.163	2.969	2.840	2.750	2.672	2.445	2.195	2.027	1.898	1.704	1.588	1.498	1.356	1.265
			k_r	→	2.066	1.936	1.872	1.807	1.743	1.549	1.420	1.291	1.162	1.033	0.968	0.904	0.775	0.651
			k_t		2.683	2.519	2.437	2.355	2.258	2.065	1.834	1.699	1.573	1.416	1.304	1.215	1.088	1.036

Acceptable-quality level class, in percent defective

Letter	Sample	n (col A)	n (col B)	k	Data
I	First	20	20	k_a	→ 3.242 2.996 2.891 2.822 2.683 2.448 2.225 2.001 1.867 1.722 1.621 1.554 1.398 1.300
				k_r	2.326 2.147 2.012 2.012 1.878 1.711 1.543 1.342 1.252 1.118 1.073 0.991 0.850 0.780
	Second	40	60	k_t	2.737 2.578 2.492 2.401 2.311 2.091 1.885 1.691 1.562 1.439 1.330 1.278 1.149 1.084
J	First	25	25	k_a	3.354 3.210 3.020 2.900 2.820 2.700 2.460 2.240 2.040 1.860 1.720 1.620 1.540 1.400 1.340
				k_r	2.520 2.400 2.220 2.160 2.100 2.000 1.800 1.610 1.460 1.320 1.200 1.114 1.040 0.920 0.880
	Second	50	75	k_t	2.916 2.783 2.598 2.506 2.425 2.327 2.107 1.905 1.721 1.570 1.438 1.339 1.270 1.149 1.085
K	First	30	30	k_a	3.286 3.131 2.921 2.812 2.733 2.611 2.373 2.191 1.981 1.826 1.671 1.570 1.470 1.351 1.282
				k_r	2.510 2.373 2.237 2.191 2.100 1.954 1.762 1.607 1.488 1.342 1.232 1.132 1.059 0.913 0.849
	Second	60	90	k_t	2.973 2.846 2.662 2.556 2.493 2.390 2.171 1.998 1.792 1.644 1.507 1.407 1.307 1.191 1.133
L	First	35	35	k_a	3.381 3.232 3.026 2.916 2.831 2.704 2.476 2.265 2.071 1.885 1.749 1.640 1.513 ← ←
				k_r	2.645 2.525 2.366 2.282 2.202 2.096 1.902 1.733 1.564 1.411 1.302 1.200 1.099 ← ←
	Second	70	105	k_t	2.967 2.830 2.645 2.557 2.484 2.376 2.166 1.986 1.810 1.644 1.518 1.415 1.298 ← ←
M	First	40	40	k_a	3.384 3.233 3.052 2.920 2.854 2.739 2.530 2.316 2.100 1.921 1.791 ← ← ← ←
				k_r	2.688 2.569 2.422 2.308 2.261 2.166 1.992 1.810 1.629 1.470 1.365 ← ← ← ←
	Second	80	120	k_t	3.003 2.871 2.702 2.582 2.520 2.419 2.237 2.040 1.835 1.666 1.552 ← ← ← ←
N	First	55	55	k_a	3.304 3.142 2.977 2.832 2.784 2.656 2.461 2.292 2.023 ← ← ← ← ← ←
				k_r	2.832 2.677 2.548 2.387 2.369 2.259 2.090 1.948 1.699 ← ← ← ← ← ←
	Second	110	165	k_t	3.036 2.908 2.736 2.635 2.577 2.460 2.269 2.102 1.861 ← ← ← ← ← ←
O	First	85	85	k_a	3.346 3.196 3.050 2.947 2.853 2.714 2.533 2.327 ← ← ← ← ← ← ←
				k_r	2.891 2.766 2.647 2.551 2.475 2.337 2.180 2.001 ← ← ← ← ← ← ←
	Second	170	255	k_t	3.119 2.975 2.831 2.733 2.646 2.527 2.350 2.151 ← ← ← ← ← ← ←

Notes:

* Variables plans for sample-size letter A are not included because their use results in little saving over the corresponding attribute plans.

↓ Use the first sampling plan below arrow. If sample size is larger than inspection-lot size, use 100 percent inspection or form larger inspection lots.

← Use the first sampling plan above arrow.

TABLE D. ACCEPTABLE QUALITY LEVEL (AQL) AND LOT TOLERANCE PERCENT DEFECTIVE (LTPD) OF SINGLE- AND DOUBLE-SAMPLING VARIABLES PLANS

Acceptable quality level class, in percent defective

Sample-size letter	.024–.035 AQL	.024–.035 LTPD	.035–.06 AQL	.035–.06 LTPD	.06–.12 AQL	.06–.12 LTPD	.12–.17 AQL	.12–.17 LTPD	.17–.22 AQL	.17–.22 LTPD	.22–.32 AQL	.22–.32 LTPD	.32–.65 AQL	.32–.65 LTPD	.65–1.2 AQL	.65–1.2 LTPD	1.2–2.2 AQL	1.2–2.2 LTPD	2.2–3.2 AQL	2.2–3.2 LTPD	3.2–4.4 AQL	3.2–4.4 LTPD	4.4–5.3 AQL	4.4–5.3 LTPD	5.3–6.4 AQL	5.3–6.4 LTPD	6.4–8.5 AQL	6.4–8.5 LTPD	8.5–11.0 AQL	8.5–11.0 LTPD
B													.50	20.73	1.00	24.68	2.00	29.57	3.00	33.05	3.50	34.52	4.40	36.89	6.40	41.24	8.50	45.10	10.50	48.32
C													.50	14.60	1.00	18.18	1.70	21.62	2.40	24.26	3.20	26.78	5.30	32.02	5.60	32.67	8.50	38.19	10.50	41.47
D													.65	12.42	1.20	15.57	1.70	17.76	2.30	19.94	3.80	24.29	4.40	25.76	6.40	30.04	7.20	31.56	10.00	36.35
E							.17	4.68	.22	6.68	.32	9.61	.65	10.28	1.00	12.25	2.00	17.01	2.90	16.68	3.20	22.00	4.50	22.94	5.90	25.76	7.20	30.04	10.00	33.33
F					.12	3.11	.17	3.67	.22	5.24	.32	7.74	.65	8.44	1.00	10.23	2.10	14.35	2.40	13.28	3.30	18.26	4.40	20.55	6.10	23.81	8.30	30.55	10.00	29.68
G					.12	2.15	.17	2.58	.22	4.14	.32	6.17	.65	6.97	1.15	9.21	1.80	12.12	2.50	11.15	3.80	17.47	4.90	18.31	5.70	20.70	7.50	26.36	9.50	27.18
H			.06	1.49	.12	1.49	.17	1.83	.22	2.97	.32	4.96	.60	5.09	1.20	7.42	2.10	9.28	2.40	10.08	4.00	15.61	4.00	16.31	6.00	18.33	7.80	26.14	9.50	23.24
I			.06	1.00	.12	1.26	.17	1.56	.22	2.14	.32	3.50	.65	4.07	1.20	5.89	2.10	8.27	3.00	9.45	4.10	14.11	4.90	15.15	6.10	15.36	7.90	24.44	9.00	20.24
J	.035	.59	.06	.82	.12	1.09	.17	1.37	.22	1.83	.32	2.67	.65	3.59	1.20	5.27	2.00	7.29	2.90	8.42	3.90	11.56	4.90	13.32	6.00	14.82	7.90	21.52	9.00	19.08
K	.035	.50	.06	.70	.12	.93	.17	1.17	.22	1.61	.32	2.31	.65	3.24	1.10	4.56	1.90	6.52	2.40	7.74	3.80	10.50	4.80	12.23	6.10	14.18	7.60	18.43	8.80	18.20
L	.035	.41	.06	.58	.12	.76	.17	1.03	.22	1.39	.32	2.05	.55	2.81	1.10	4.09	1.80	5.72	2.70	7.06	3.60	9.56	4.80	11.24	6.20	13.44	8.80	17.61		
M	.035	.35	.06	.50	.11	.64	.17	.88	.21	1.19	.30	1.78	.55	2.32	1.00	3.51	1.75	5.20												
N	.035	.28	.06	.42	.11	.43	.14	.56	.20	.99	.30	1.52	.55	2.04	.90	2.91	1.80	4.81												
O	.035	.19	.06	.29					.19	.71	.30	1.32	.50	1.49	.90	2.34														

Notes:

(1) The acceptable quality level (AQL) is the percentage of defective items in an inspection lot such that the sampling plan will accept 95 percent of all lots submitted containing that percentage of defects.

(2) The lot tolerance percent defective (LTPD) is the percentage of defective items in an inspection lot such that the sampling plan will reject 90 percent of all lots submitted containing that percentage of defects.

TABLE E

SINGLE- AND DOUBLE-SAMPLING PLANS AND OPERATING-CHARACTERISTIC CURVES, CLASSIFIED BY SAMPLE-SIZE LETTER, ACCEPTABLE-QUALITY LEVEL, AND AVERAGE OUTGOING-QUALITY LIMIT

TABLE E

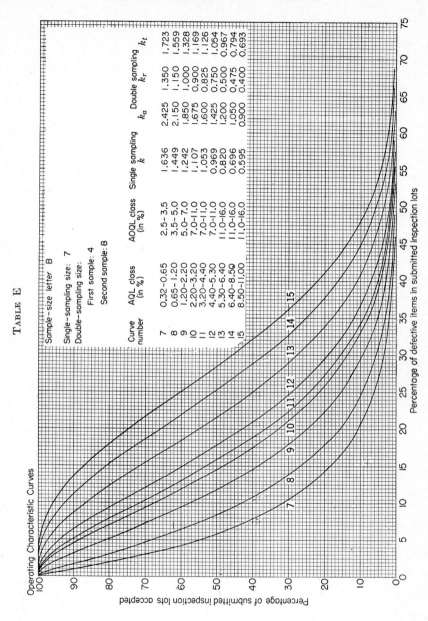

Operating Characteristic Curves

Sample-size letter B

Single-sampling size: 7
Double-sampling size:
    First sample: 4
    Second sample: 8

Curve number	AQL class (in %)	AOQL class (in %)	Single sampling k	Double sampling k_a	k_r	k_t
7	0.32–0.65	2.5–3.5	1.636	2.425	1.350	1.723
8	0.65–1.20	3.5–5.0	1.449	2.150	1.150	1.559
9	1.20–2.20	5.0–7.0	1.242	1.850	1.000	1.328
10	2.20–3.20	7.0–11.0	1.107	1.675	0.900	1.169
11	3.20–4.40	7.0–11.0	1.053	1.600	0.825	1.126
12	4.40–5.30	7.0–11.0	0.969	1.425	0.750	1.054
13	5.30–6.40	11.0–16.0	0.820	1.200	0.500	0.967
14	6.40–8.50	11.0–16.0	0.696	1.050	0.475	0.794
15	8.50–11.00	11.0–16.0	0.595	0.900	0.400	0.693

Percentage of submitted inspection lots accepted

Percentage of defective items in submitted inspection lots

TABLE E.—(*Continued*).

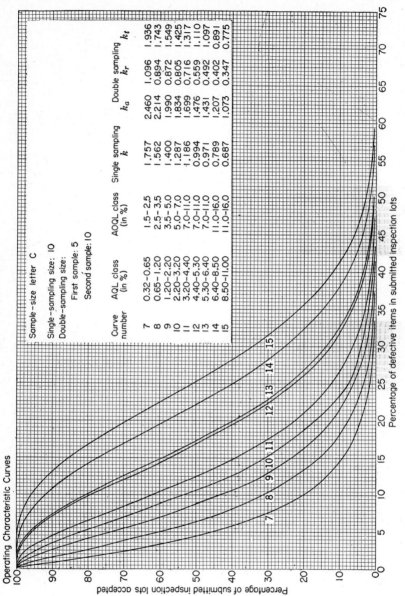

Operating Characteristic Curves

Sample-size letter C

Single-sampling size: 10
Double-sampling size:
First sample: 5
Second sample: 10

Curve number	AQL class (in %)	AOQL class (in %)	Single sampling k	Double sampling k_a	k_r	k_t
7	0.32–0.65	1.5–2.5	1.757	2.460	1.096	1.936
8	0.65–1.20	2.5–3.5	1.562	2.214	0.894	1.743
9	1.20–2.20	3.5–5.0	1.400	1.990	0.872	1.549
10	2.20–3.20	5.0–7.0	1.287	1.834	0.805	1.425
11	3.20–4.40	7.0–11.0	1.186	1.699	0.716	1.317
12	4.40–5.30	7.0–11.0	0.994	1.476	0.559	1.110
13	5.30–6.40	7.0–11.0	0.971	1.431	0.492	1.097
14	6.40–8.50	11.0–16.0	0.789	1.207	0.402	0.891
15	8.50–11.00	11.0–16.0	0.687	1.073	0.347	0.775

Percentage of defective items in submitted inspection lots

Percentage of submitted inspection lots accepted

TABLE E.—(Continued)

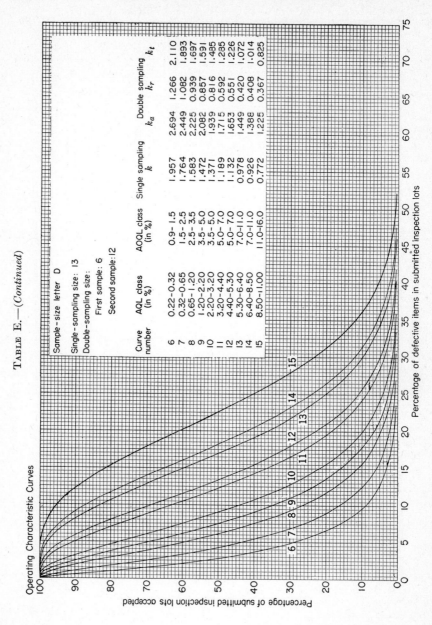

Operating Characteristic Curves

Sample-size letter D

Single-sampling size: 13
Double-sampling size:
   First sample: 6
   Second sample: 12

Curve number	AQL class (in %)	AOQL class (in %)	Single sampling k	Double sampling k_a	Double sampling k_r	Double sampling k_t
6	0.22–0.32	0.9–1.5	1.957	2.694	1.266	2.110
7	0.32–0.65	1.5–2.5	1.764	2.449	1.082	1.893
8	0.65–1.20	2.5–3.5	1.583	2.225	0.939	1.697
9	1.20–2.20	3.5–5.0	1.472	2.082	0.857	1.591
10	2.20–3.20	3.5–5.0	1.371	1.939	0.816	1.485
11	3.20–4.40	5.0–7.0	1.189	1.715	0.592	1.285
12	4.40–5.30	5.0–7.0	1.132	1.653	0.551	1.226
13	5.30–6.40	7.0–11.0	0.978	1.449	0.420	1.072
14	6.40–8.50	7.0–11.0	0.926	1.388	0.408	1.014
15	8.50–1.00	11.0–16.0	0.772	1.225	0.367	0.825

Percentage of submitted inspection lots accepted

Percentage of defective items in submitted inspection lots

Table E.—(Continued)

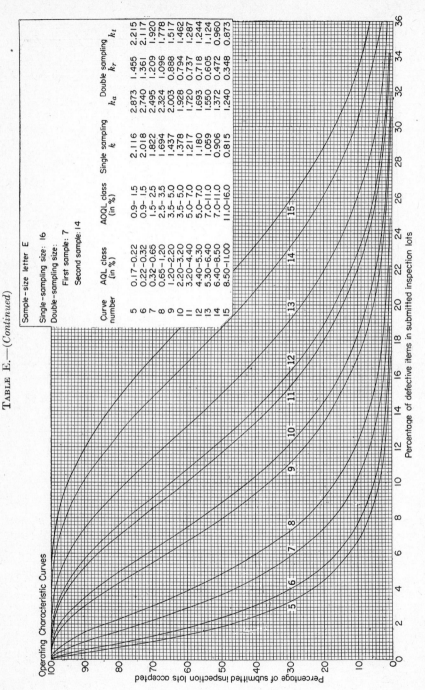

Operating Characteristic Curves

Sample-size letter E

Single-sampling size: 16
Double-sampling size:
    First sample: 7
    Second sample: 14

Curve number	AQL class (in %)	AOQL class (in %)	Single sampling k	Double sampling k_a	k_r	k_t
5	0.17–0.22	0.9–1.5	2.116	2.873	1.455	2.215
6	0.22–0.32	0.9–1.5	2.018	2.740	1.361	2.117
7	0.32–0.65	1.5–2.5	1.822	2.495	1.209	1.920
8	0.65–1.20	2.5–3.5	1.694	2.324	1.096	1.778
9	1.20–2.20	3.5–5.0	1.437	2.003	0.888	1.517
10	2.20–3.20	3.5–5.0	1.378	1.928	0.794	1.462
11	3.20–4.40	5.0–7.0	1.217	1.720	0.737	1.287
12	4.40–5.30	5.0–7.0	1.180	1.693	0.718	1.244
13	5.30–6.40	7.0–11.0	1.059	1.550	0.605	1.124
14	6.40–8.50	7.0–11.0	0.906	1.372	0.472	0.960
15	8.50–11.00	11.0–16.0	0.815	1.240	0.348	0.873

Percentage of submitted inspection lots accepted

Percentage of defective items in submitted inspection lots

TABLE E.—(Continued)

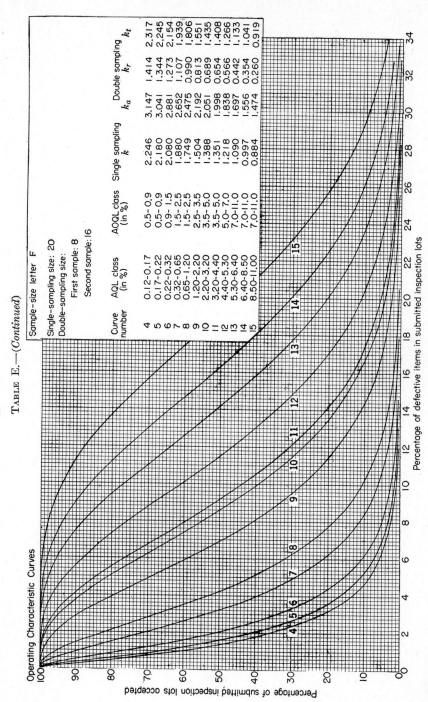

Operating Characteristic Curves

Sample-size letter F

Single-sampling size: 20
Double-sampling size:
  First sample: 8
  Second sample: 16

Curve number	AQL class (in %)	AOQL class (in %)	Single sampling k	Double sampling k_a	k_r	k_t
4	0.12-0.17	0.5-0.9	2.246	3.147	1.414	2.317
5	0.17-0.22	0.5-0.9	2.180	3.041	1.344	2.245
6	0.22-0.32	0.9-1.5	2.080	2.881	1.273	2.154
7	0.32-0.65	1.5-2.5	1.880	2.652	1.107	1.939
8	0.65-1.20	1.5-2.5	1.749	2.475	0.990	1.806
9	1.20-2.20	2.5-3.5	1.504	2.192	0.813	1.551
10	2.20-3.20	3.5-5.0	1.388	2.051	0.689	1.435
11	3.20-4.40	3.5-5.0	1.351	1.998	0.654	1.408
12	4.40-5.30	5.0-7.0	1.218	1.838	0.566	1.266
13	5.30-6.40	7.0-11.0	1.090	1.697	0.442	1.133
14	6.40-8.50	7.0-11.0	0.997	1.556	0.354	1.041
15	8.50-11.00	7.0-11.0	0.884	1.474	0.260	0.919

Percentage of submitted inspection lots accepted

Percentage of defective items in submitted inspection lots

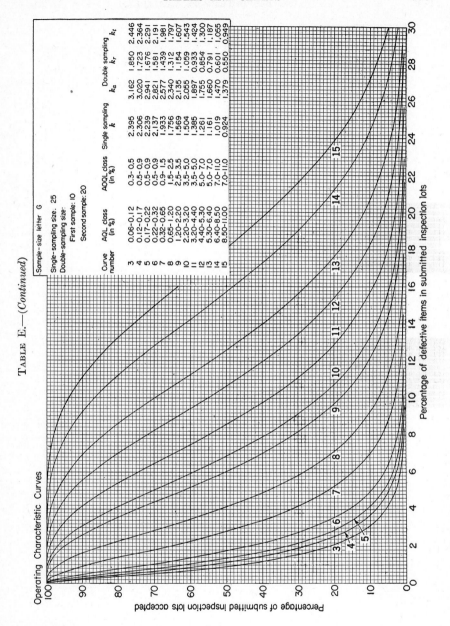

TABLE E.—(Continued)

Operating Characteristic Curves

		AQL class (in %)	AOQL class (in %)	Single sampling k	Double sampling k_a	k_r	k_t
Curve number							
3	0.06–0.12		0.3–0.5	2.395	3.162	1.850	2.446
4	0.12–0.17		0.5–0.9	2.306	3.020	1.723	2.364
5	0.17–0.22		0.5–0.9	2.239	2.941	1.676	2.291
6	0.22–0.32		0.5–0.9	2.137	2.821	1.581	2.191
7	0.32–0.65		0.9–1.5	1.933	2.577	1.439	1.981
8	0.65–1.20		1.5–2.5	1.756	2.340	1.312	1.797
9	1.20–2.20		2.5–3.5	1.569	2.135	1.154	1.607
10	2.20–3.20		3.5–5.0	1.504	2.055	1.059	1.543
11	3.20–4.40		3.5–5.0	1.385	1.897	0.933	1.424
12	4.40–5.30		5.0–7.0	1.261	1.755	0.854	1.300
13	5.30–6.40		5.0–7.0	1.161	1.660	0.791	1.187
14	6.40–8.50		7.0–11.0	1.019	1.470	0.601	1.055
15	8.50–11.00		7.0–11.0	0.924	1.379	0.550	0.949

Sample-size letter G
Single-sampling size. 25
Double-sampling size:
First sample: 10
Second sample: 20

Percentage of defective items in submitted inspection lots

Percentage of submitted inspection lots accepted

TABLE E.—(*Continued*)

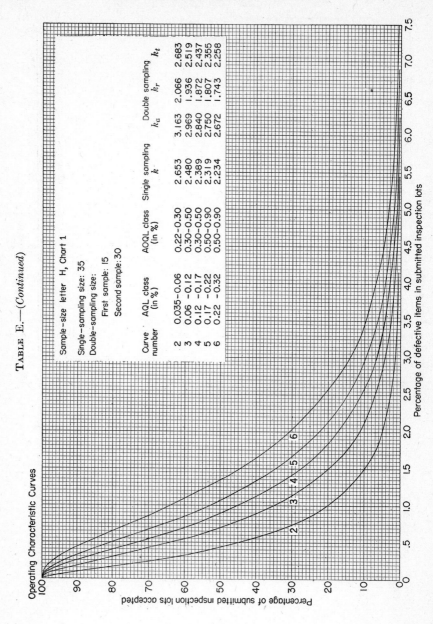

Operating Characteristic Curves

Sample–size letter H, Chart 1

Single–sampling size: 35
Double–sampling size:
　First sample: 15
　Second sample: 30

Curve number	AQL class (in %)	AOQL class (in %)	Single sampling k	Double sampling k_a	k_r	k_t
2	0.035–0.06	0.22–0.30	2.653	3.163	2.066	2.683
3	0.06 –0.12	0.30–0.50	2.480	2.969	1.936	2.519
4	0.12 –0.17	0.30–0.50	2.389	2.840	1.872	2.437
5	0.17 –0.22	0.50–0.90	2.319	2.750	1.807	2.355
6	0.22 –0.32	0.50–0.90	2.234	2.672	1.743	2.258

Percentage of submitted inspection lots accepted

Percentage of defective items in submitted inspection lots

TABLE E.—(*Continued*)

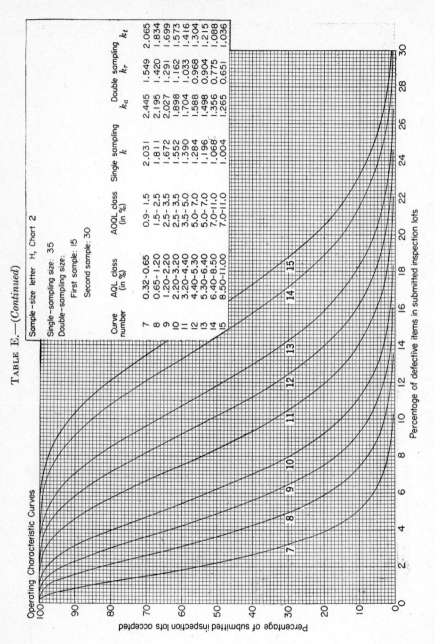

Operating Characteristic Curves

Sample-size letter H, Chart 2

Single-sampling size: 35
Double-sampling size:
First sample: 15
Second sample: 30

Curve number	AQL class (in %)	AOQL class (in %)	Single sampling k	Double sampling k_a	k_r	k_t
7	0.32-0.65	0.9-1.5	2.031	2.445	1.549	2.065
8	0.65-1.20	1.5-2.5	1.811	2.195	1.420	1.834
9	1.20-2.20	2.5-3.5	1.672	2.027	1.291	1.699
10	2.20-3.20	2.5-3.5	1.552	1.898	1.162	1.573
11	3.20-4.40	3.5-5.0	1.390	1.704	1.033	1.416
12	4.40-5.30	5.0-7.0	1.284	1.588	0.968	1.304
13	5.30-6.40	5.0-7.0	1.196	1.498	0.904	1.215
14	6.40-8.50	7.0-11.0	1.068	1.356	0.775	1.088
15	8.50-11.00	7.0-11.0	1.004	1.265	0.651	1.036

Percentage of submitted inspection lots accepted

Percentage of defective items in submitted inspection lots

TABLE E.—(*Continued*)

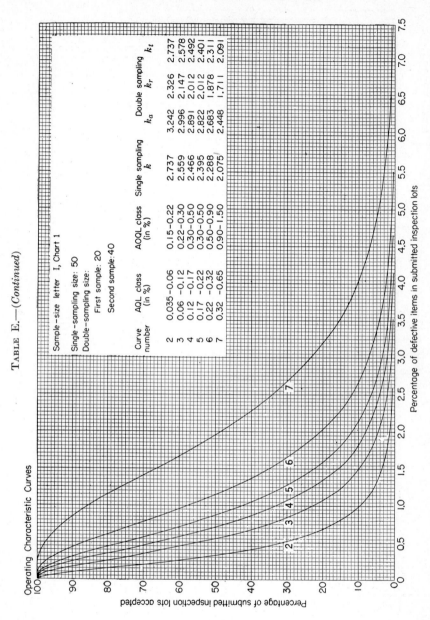

Operating Characteristic Curves

Sample–size letter I, Chart 1

Single–sampling size: 50
Double–sampling size:
    First sample: 20
    Second sample: 40

Curve number	AQL class (in %)	AOQL class (in %)	Single sampling k	Double sampling k_a	Double sampling k_r	Double sampling k_t
2	0.035–0.06	0.15–0.22	2.737	3.242	2.326	2.737
3	0.06 –0.12	0.22–0.30	2.559	2.996	2.147	2.578
4	0.12 –0.17	0.30–0.50	2.466	2.891	2.012	2.492
5	0.17 –0.22	0.30–0.50	2.395	2.822	2.012	2.401
6	0.22 –0.32	0.50–0.90	2.288	2.683	1.878	2.311
7	0.32 –0.65	0.90–1.50	2.075	2.448	1.711	2.091

Percentage of defective items in submitted inspection lots

Percentage of submitted inspection lots accepted

TABLE E.—*(Continued)*

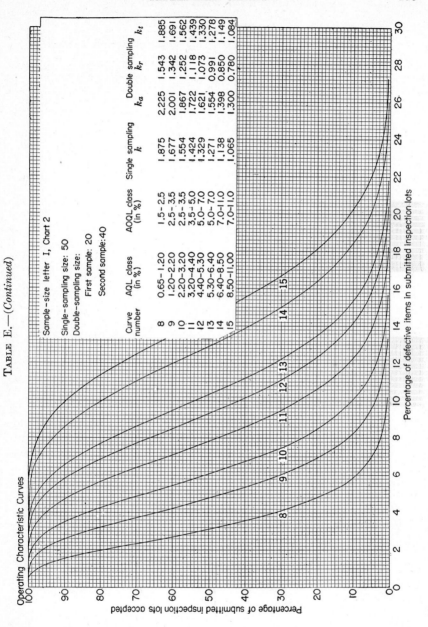

Operating Characteristic Curves

Sample-size letter I, Chart 2

Single-sampling size: 50
Double-sampling size:
    First sample: 20
    Second sample: 40

Curve number	AQL class (in %)	AQQL class (in %)	Single sampling k	Double sampling k_a	Double sampling k_r	Double sampling k_t
8	0.65–1.20	1.5–2.5	1.875	2.225	1.543	1.885
9	1.20–2.20	2.5–3.5	1.677	2.001	1.342	1.691
10	2.20–3.20	2.5–3.5	1.554	1.867	1.252	1.562
11	3.20–4.40	3.5–5.0	1.424	1.722	1.118	1.439
12	4.40–5.30	5.0–7.0	1.329	1.621	1.073	1.330
13	5.30–6.40	5.0–7.0	1.271	1.554	0.991	1.278
14	6.40–8.50	7.0–11.0	1.138	1.398	0.850	1.149
15	8.50–11.00	7.0–11.0	1.065	1.300	0.780	1.084

Percentage of defective items in submitted inspection lots

Percentage of submitted inspection lots accepted

TABLE E.—(Continued)

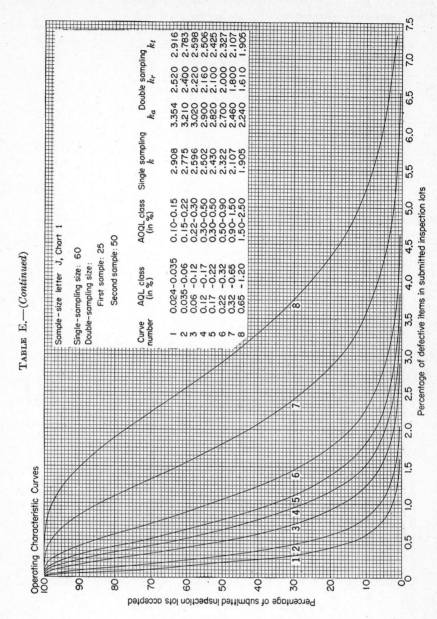

Operating Characteristic Curves

Sample-size letter J, Chart 1

Single-sampling size: 60
Double-sampling size:
　　First sample: 25
　　Second sample: 50

Curve number	AQL class (in %)	AOQL class (in %)	Single sampling k	Double sampling k_a	Double sampling k_r	Double sampling k_t
1	0.024-0.035	0.10-0.15	2.908	3.354	2.520	2.916
2	0.035-0.06	0.15-0.22	2.775	3.210	2.400	2.783
3	0.06 -0.12	0.22-0.30	2.596	3.020	2.220	2.598
4	0.12 -0.17	0.30-0.50	2.502	2.900	2.160	2.506
5	0.17 -0.22	0.30-0.50	2.430	2.820	2.100	2.425
6	0.22 -0.32	0.50-0.90	2.322	2.700	2.000	2.327
7	0.32 -0.65	0.90-1.50	2.107	2.460	1.800	2.107
8	0.65 -1.20	1.50-2.50	1.905	2.240	1.610	1.905

Percentage of submitted inspection lots accepted

Percentage of defective items in submitted inspection lots

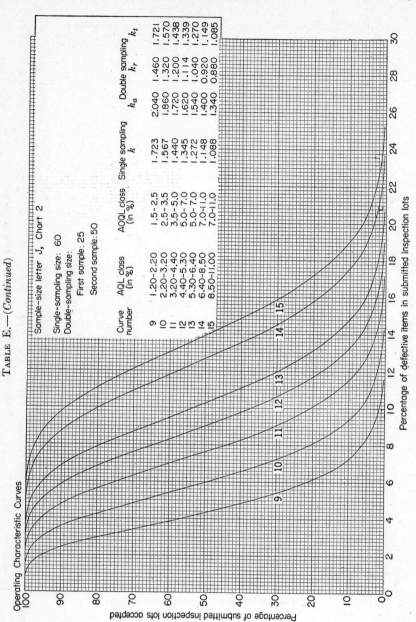

TABLE E.—(*Continued*)

Operating Characteristic Curves

Sample-size letter J, Chart 2

Single-sampling size: 60
Double-sampling size:
First sample: 25
Second sample: 50

Curve number	AQL class (in %)	AOQL class (in %)	Single sampling k	Double sampling k_a	k_r	k_t
9	1.20–2.20	1.5–2.5	1.723	2.040	1.460	1.721
10	2.20–3.20	2.5–3.5	1.567	1.860	1.320	1.570
11	3.20–4.40	3.5–5.0	1.440	1.720	1.200	1.438
12	4.40–5.30	5.0–7.0	1.345	1.620	1.114	1.339
13	5.30–6.40	5.0–7.0	1.272	1.540	1.040	1.270
14	6.40–8.50	7.0–11.0	1.148	1.400	0.920	1.149
15	8.50–11.00	7.0–11.0	1.088	1.340	0.880	1.085

Percentage of submitted inspection lots accepted

Percentage of defective items in submitted inspection lots

TABLE E.—(*Continued*)

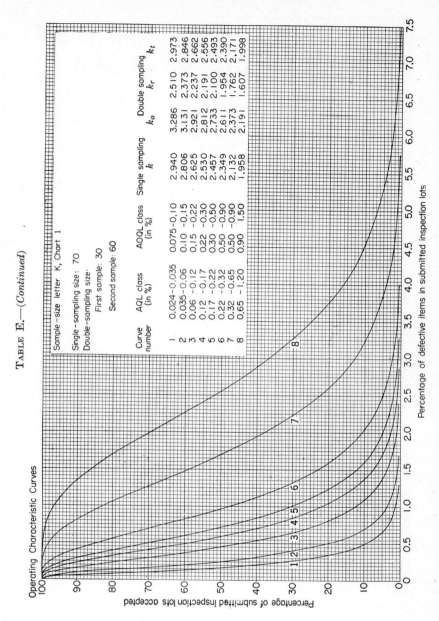

Operating Characteristic Curves

Sample-size letter K, Chart 1
Single-sampling size: 70
Double-sampling size:
First sample: 30
Second sample: 60

Curve number	AQL class (in %)	AOQL class (in %)	Single sampling k	Double sampling k_a	k_r	k_t
1	0.024-0.035	0.075-0.10	2.940	3.286	2.510	2.973
2	0.035-0.06	0.10 -0.15	2.806	3.131	2.373	2.846
3	0.06 -0.12	0.15 -0.22	2.625	2.921	2.237	2.662
4	0.12 -0.17	0.22 -0.30	2.530	2.812	2.191	2.556
5	0.17 -0.22	0.30 -0.50	2.457	2.733	2.100	2.493
6	0.22 -0.32	0.50 -0.90	2.349	2.611	1.954	2.390
7	0.32 -0.65	0.50 -0.90	2.132	2.373	1.762	2.171
8	0.65 -1.20	0.90 -1.50	1.958	2.191	1.607	1.998

Percentage of defective items in submitted inspection lots

Percentage of submitted inspection lots accepted

TABLE E.—(*Continued*)

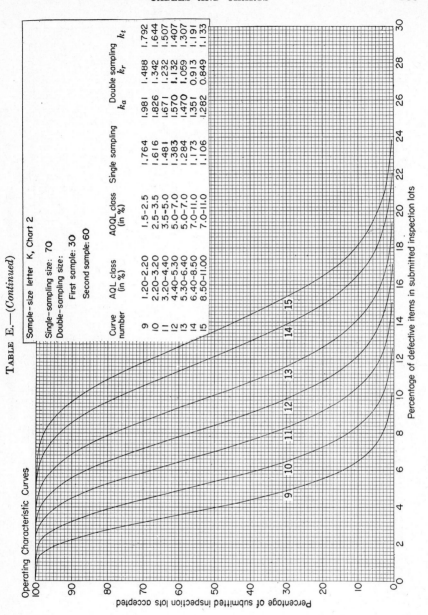

Operating Characteristic Curves

Sample-size letter K, Chart 2

Single-sampling size: 70
Double-sampling size:

First sample: 30
Second sample: 60

Curve number	AQL class (in %)	AOQL class (in %)	Single sampling	Double sampling k_a	k_r	k_t
9	1.20–2.20	1.5–2.5	1.764	1.981	1.488	1.792
10	2.20–3.20	2.5–3.5	1.616	1.826	1.342	1.644
11	3.20–4.40	3.5–5.0	1.481	1.671	1.232	1.507
12	4.40–5.30	5.0–7.0	1.383	1.570	1.132	1.407
13	5.30–6.40	5.0–7.0	1.284	1.470	1.059	1.307
14	6.40–8.50	7.0–11.0	1.173	1.351	0.913	1.191
15	8.50–11.00	7.0–11.0	1.106	1.282	0.849	1.133

Percentage of defective items in submitted inspection lots

Percentage of submitted inspection lots accepted

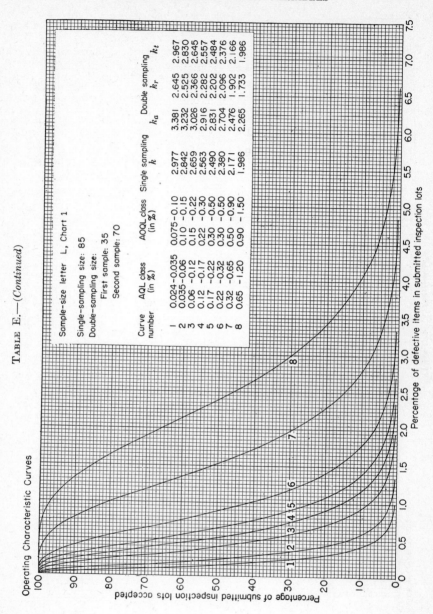

TABLE E.—(*Continued*)

Operating Characteristic Curves

Sample-size letter L, Chart 1

Single-sampling size: 85

Double-sampling size:
First sample: 35
Second sample: 70

Curve number	AQL class (in %)	AOQL class (in %)	Single sampling k	Double sampling k_a	k_r	k_t
1	0.024–0.035	0.075–0.10	2.977	3.381	2.645	2.967
2	0.035–0.06	0.10 –0.15	2.842	3.232	2.525	2.830
3	0.06 –0.12	0.15 –0.22	2.659	3.026	2.366	2.645
4	0.12 –0.17	0.22 –0.30	2.563	2.916	2.282	2.557
5	0.17 –0.22	0.30 –0.50	2.490	2.831	2.202	2.484
6	0.22 –0.32	0.30 –0.50	2.380	2.704	2.096	2.376
7	0.32 –0.65	0.50 –0.90	2.171	2.476	1.902	2.166
8	0.65 –1.20	0.90 –1.50	1.986	2.265	1.733	1.986

Percentage of defective items in submitted inspection lots

Percentage of submitted inspection lots accepted

TABLE E.—(*Continued*)

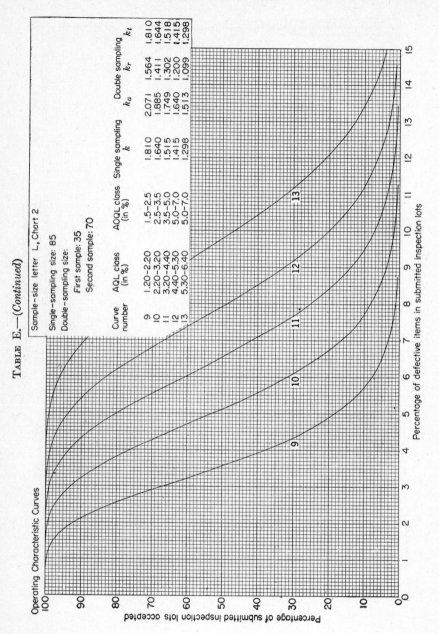

Operating Characteristic Curves

Sample-size letter L, Chart 2

Single-sampling size: 85
Double-sampling size:
 First sample: 35
 Second sample: 70

Curve number	AQL class (in %)	AOQL class (in %)	Single sampling k	Double sampling k_a	Double sampling k_r	Double sampling k_t
9	1.20–2.20	1.5–2.5	1.810	2.071	1.564	1.810
10	2.20–3.20	2.5–3.5	1.640	1.885	1.411	1.644
11	3.20–4.40	3.5–5.0	1.515	1.749	1.302	1.518
12	4.40–5.30	5.0–7.0	1.415	1.640	1.200	1.415
13	5.30–6.40	5.0–7.0	1.298	1.513	1.099	1.298

Percentage of submitted inspection lots accepted

Percentage of defective items in submitted inspection lots

TABLE E.—(*Continued*)

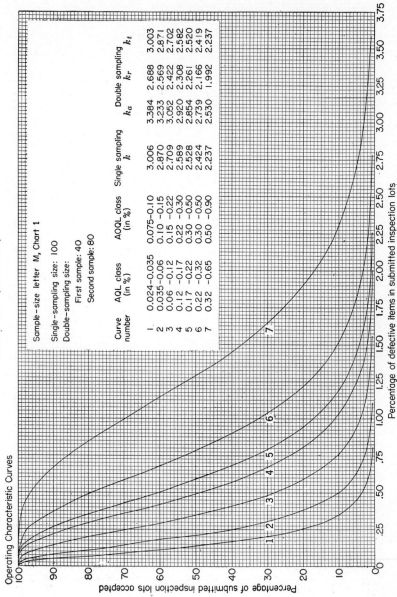

Operating Characteristic Curves

Sample-size letter M, Chart 1

Single-sampling size: 100
Double-sampling size:
   First sample: 40
   Second sample: 80

Curve number	AQL class (in %)	AOQL class (in %)	Single sampling k	Double sampling k_a	k_r	k_t
1	0.024–0.035	0.075–0.10	3.006	3.384	2.688	3.003
2	0.035–0.06	0.10 –0.15	2.870	3.233	2.569	2.871
3	0.06 –0.12	0.15 –0.22	2.709	3.052	2.422	2.702
4	0.12 –0.17	0.22 –0.30	2.589	2.920	2.308	2.582
5	0.17 –0.22	0.30 –0.50	2.528	2.854	2.261	2.520
6	0.22 –0.32	0.30 –0.50	2.424	2.739	2.166	2.419
7	0.32 –0.65	0.50 –0.90	2.237	2.530	1.992	2.237

Percentage of defective items in submitted inspection lots

Percentage of submitted inspection lots accepted

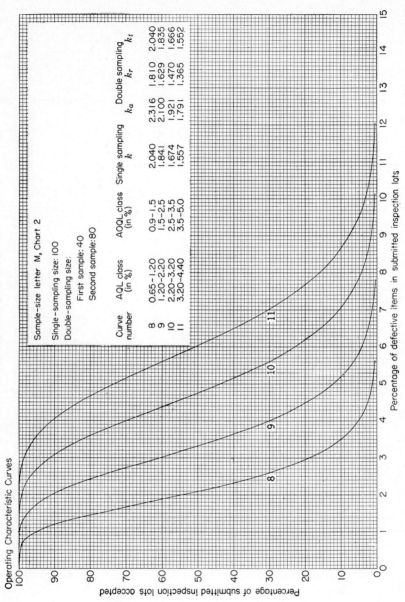

Table E.—(Continued)

Operating Characteristic Curves

Sample-size letter M, Chart 2

Single-sampling size: 100
Double-sampling size:
    First sample: 40
    Second sample: 80

Curve number	AQL class (in %)	AOQL class6 (in %)	Single sampling k	Double sampling k_a	k_r	k_t
8	0.65–1.20	0.9–1.5	2.040	2.316	1.810	2.040
9	1.20–2.20	1.5–2.5	1.841	2.100	1.629	1.835
10	2.20–3.20	2.5–3.5	1.674	1.921	1.470	1.666
11	3.20–4.40	3.5–5.0	1.557	1.791	1.365	1.552

Percentage of submitted inspection lots accepted

Percentage of defective items in submitted inspection lots

TABLE E.—(Continued)

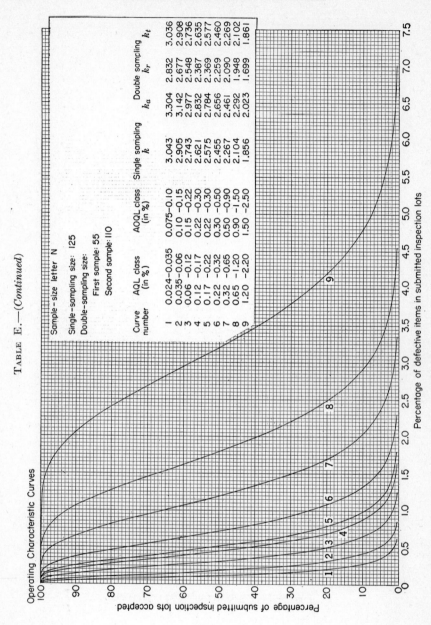

Operating Characteristic Curves

Sample-size letter N

Single-sampling size: 125

Double-sampling size:

First sample: 55

Second sample: 110

Curve number	AQL class (in %)	AOQL class (in %)	Single sampling k	Double sampling k_a	k_r	k_t
1	0.024-0.035	0.075-0.10	3.043	3.304	2.832	3.036
2	0.035-0.06	0.10 -0.15	2.905	3.142	2.677	2.908
3	0.06 -0.12	0.15 -0.22	2.743	2.977	2.548	2.736
4	0.12 -0.17	0.22 -0.30	2.621	2.832	2.387	2.635
5	0.17 -0.22	0.22 -0.30	2.575	2.784	2.369	2.577
6	0.22 -0.32	0.30 -0.50	2.455	2.656	2.259	2.460
7	0.32 -0.65	0.50 -0.90	2.267	2.461	2.090	2.269
8	0.65 -1.20	0.90 -1.50	2.104	2.292	1.948	2.102
9	1.20 -2.20	1.50 -2.50	1.856	2.023	1.699	1.861

Percentage of submitted inspection lots accepted

Percentage of defective items in submitted inspection lots

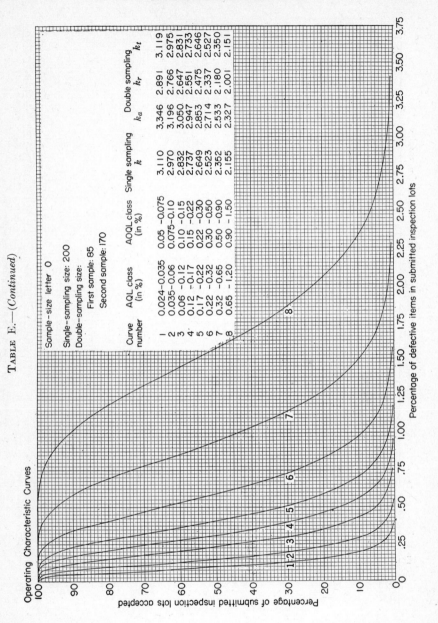

TABLE E.—(Continued)

Operating Characteristic Curves

Sample-size letter O

Single-sampling size: 200
Double-sampling size:
   First sample: 85
   Second sample: 170

Curve number	AQL class (in %)	AOQL class (in %)	Single sampling k	Double sampling k_a	k_r	k_t
1	0.024–0.035	0.05 –0.075	3.110	3.346	2.891	3.119
2	0.035–0.06	0.075–0.10	2.970	3.196	2.766	2.975
3	0.06 –0.12	0.10 –0.15	2.832	3.050	2.647	2.831
4	0.12 –0.17	0.15 –0.22	2.737	2.947	2.551	2.733
5	0.17 –0.22	0.22 –0.30	2.649	2.853	2.475	2.646
6	0.22 –0.32	0.30 –0.50	2.523	2.714	2.337	2.527
7	0.32 –0.65	0.50 –0.90	2.352	2.533	2.180	2.350
8	0.65 –1.20	0.90 –1.50	2.155	2.327	2.001	2.151

Percentage of submitted inspection lots accepted

Percentage of defective items in submitted inspection lots

TABLE F. CONSTANTS FOR THE OPTIONAL SINGLE-SAMPLING ACCEPTANCE CRITERION

Sample-size letter	Constant							Acceptable-quality level class, in percent defective								
		.024–.035	.035–.06	.06–.12	.12–.17	.17–.22	.22–.32	.32–.65	.65–1.2	1.2–2.2	2.2–3.2	3.2–4.4	4.4–5.3	5.3–6.4	6.4–8.5	8.5–11.0
B	k_w	→	→	→	→	→	→	1.632	1.936	2.360	2.696	2.845	3.094	3.588	4.042	4.431
	k_x							0.189	0.201	0.222	0.243	0.253	0.273	0.325	0.396	0.489
	k_y							0.640	0.816	1.111	1.399	1.546	1.826	2.550	3.539	4.842
	k_z							2.242	2.858	3.890	4.896	5.411	6.390	8.923	12.386	16.948
C	k_w	→	→	→	→	→	→	2.202	2.616	3.041	3.388	3.740	4.527	4.632	5.547	6.114
	k_x							0.129	0.137	0.146	0.154	0.164	0.191	0.195	0.245	0.291
	k_y							0.583	0.738	0.918	1.087	1.280	1.822	1.909	2.891	3.814
	k_z							2.915	3.689	4.592	5.434	6.398	9.109	9.546	14.457	19.069
D	k_w	→	→	→	→	→	2.485	2.919	3.423	3.789	4.167	4.972	5.260	6.133	6.460	7.519
	k_x						0.0955	0.0997	0.105	0.110	0.115	0.127	0.132	0.151	0.160	0.196
	k_y						0.482	0.593	0.737	0.852	0.982	1.306	1.441	1.930	2.153	3.098
	k_z						3.133	3.856	4.789	5.538	6.384	8.488	9.365	12.546	13.995	20.135
E	k_w	→	→	→	→	2.738	2.957	3.472	3.876	4.894	5.174	6.046	6.270	7.071	8.238	9.013
	k_x					0.0756	0.0769	0.0802	0.0829	0.0909	0.0934	0.102	0.105	0.115	0.134	0.151
	k_y					0.419	0.460	0.565	0.653	0.908	0.987	1.266	1.347	1.672	2.284	2.823
	k_z					3.350	3.683	4.519	5.227	7.264	7.899	10.128	10.773	13.375	18.274	22.583
F	k_w	→	→	→	3.143	3.303	3.567	4.190	4.681	5.825	6.492	6.725	7.650	8.683	9.529	10.665
	k_x				0.0594	0.0600	0.0610	0.0634	0.0655	0.0710	0.0747	0.0760	0.0820	0.0900	0.0978	0.111
	k_y				0.377	0.400	0.439	0.538	0.621	0.840	0.986	1.041	1.281	1.599	1.911	2.431
	k_z				3.766	3.998	4.392	5.376	6.211	8.400	9.862	10.410	12.807	15.992	19.115	24.314
G	k_w	→	→	3.563	3.799	3.991	4.311	5.067	5.877	6.933	7.357	8.224	9.266	10.222	11.774	12.947
	k_x			0.0467	0.0472	0.0477	0.0484	0.0503	0.0525	0.0556	0.0570	0.0600	0.0641	0.0685	0.0770	0.0850
	k_y			0.335	0.361	0.383	0.420	0.514	0.623	0.780	0.849	1.001	1.207	1.424	1.849	2.249
	k_z			4.184	4.513	4.787	5.255	6.423	7.783	9.749	10.610	12.512	15.093	17.805	23.113	28.110
H	k_w	→	4.230	4.755	5.069	5.331	5.675	6.634	7.944	8.958	9.974	11.596	12.837	13.989	15.883	16.932
	k_x		0.0325	0.0331	0.0334	0.0337	0.0341	0.0353	0.0370	0.0385	0.0401	0.0429	0.0454	0.0480	0.0529	0.0561
	k_y		0.276	0.316	0.340	0.361	0.389	0.471	0.592	0.695	0.807	1.006	1.178	1.358	1.703	1.927
	k_z		4.831	5.528	5.957	6.322	6.813	8.243	10.367	12.162	14.115	17.597	20.623	23.769	29.808	33.730

		→	5.771	6.491	6.920	7.274	7.859	9.235	10.851	12.853	14.349	16.183	17.714	18.735	21.350	22.959
I	k_w		5.771	6.491	6.920	7.274	7.859	9.235	10.851	12.853	14.349	16.183	17.714	18.735	21.350	22.959
	k_x		0.0226	0.0230	0.0232	0.0234	0.0237	0.0246	0.0256	0.0270	0.0281	0.0297	0.0311	0.0321	0.0351	0.0373
	k_y		0.262	0.299	0.322	0.342	0.374	0.455	0.558	0.697	0.812	0.967	1.110	1.213	1.513	1.728
	k_z		6.541	7.483	8.058	8.543	9.360	11.380	13.938	17.423	20.291	24.164	27.743	30.332	37.837	43.201
J	k_w	6.239	6.781	7.624	8.127	8.545	9.231	10.847	12.746	14.866	17.074	19.196	21.004	22.536	25.454	27.018
	k_x	0.0186	0.0188	0.0191	0.0193	0.0194	0.0197	0.0204	0.0212	0.0222	0.0233	0.0246	0.0257	0.0268	0.0291	0.0305
	k_y	0.233	0.255	0.292	0.314	0.333	0.365	0.443	0.542	0.662	0.801	0.948	1.087	1.216	1.492	1.661
	k_z	6.977	7.662	8.755	9.425	9.992	10.943	13.290	16.258	19.874	24.028	28.453	32.614	36.465	44.768	49.842
K	k_w	7.155	7.776	8.745	9.323	9.806	10.586	12.443	14.275	16.781	19.106	21.607	23.689	26.051	29.041	31.036
	k_x	0.0159	0.0161	0.0163	0.0165	0.0166	0.0168	0.0174	0.0180	0.0188	0.0197	0.0207	0.0216	0.0228	0.0245	0.0258
	k_y	0.228	0.250	0.286	0.308	0.327	0.357	0.434	0.514	0.634	0.755	0.899	1.031	1.196	1.433	1.612
	k_z	7.983	8.763	10.014	10.780	11.430	12.505	15.180	17.998	22.174	26.422	31.459	36.075	41.852	50.148	56.408
L	k_w	8.517	9.254	10.409	11.098	11.667	12.604	14.703	16.990	19.644	22.767	25.491	27.979	31.287	←	
	k_x	0.0131	0.0132	0.0134	0.0135	0.0136	0.0138	0.0142	0.0147	0.0153	0.0161	0.0168	0.0176	0.0187		
	k_y	0.223	0.245	0.280	0.301	0.319	0.349	0.419	0.501	0.603	0.735	0.861	0.987	1.173		
	k_z	9.478	10.400	11.881	12.787	13.548	14.829	17.822	21.297	25.640	31.231	36.598	41.593	49.857		
M	k_w	9.864	10.718	11.872	12.852	13.395	14.398	16.489	19.180	22.555	26.037	28.911	←			
	k_x	0.0111	0.0112	0.0113	0.0115	0.0115	0.0117	0.0120	0.0124	0.0129	0.0135	0.0141				
	k_y	0.219	0.240	0.270	0.295	0.310	0.337	0.396	0.476	0.584	0.707	0.817				
	k_z	10.956	12.019	13.490	14.770	15.491	16.849	19.784	23.789	29.210	35.328	40.837				
N	k_w	12.086	13.137	14.547	15.757	16.250	17.646	20.198	22.849	27.898	←					
	k_x	0.00886	0.00894	0.00905	0.00916	0.00920	0.00932	0.00954	0.00979	0.0103						
	k_y	0.214	0.235	0.264	0.289	0.299	0.329	0.386	0.448	0.576						
	k_z	13.391	14.694	16.480	18.050	18.701	20.574	24.128	28.011	35.997						
O	k_w	18.647	20.263	22.062	23.436	24.822	27.018	30.466	35.259	←						
	k_x	0.00551	0.00556	0.00562	0.00566	0.00571	0.00578	0.00590	0.00607							
	k_y	0.206	0.226	0.248	0.266	0.284	0.313	0.360	0.429							
	k_z	20.575	22.560	24.812	26.565	28.359	31.262	35.973	42.851							

Notes:
→ Use the first sampling plan below arrow. If sample size is larger than inspection-lot size, use 100 percent inspection or form larger inspection lots.
↑ Use the first sampling plan above arrow.

CHART G. ESTIMATED PROCESS AVERAGE AS A FUNCTION OF k (PART I)

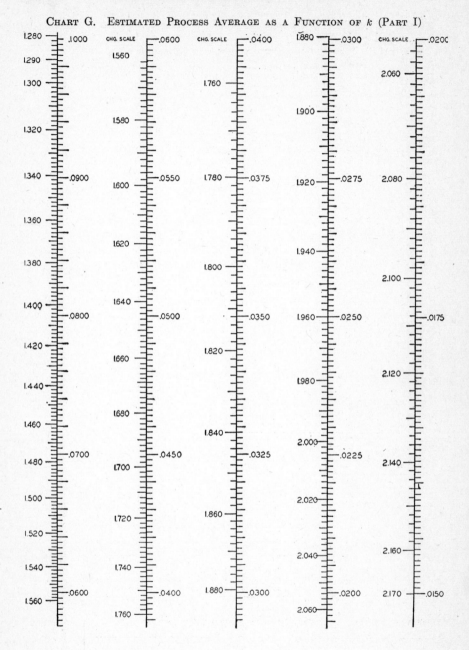

Chart G. Estimated Process Average as a Function of k (Part II)

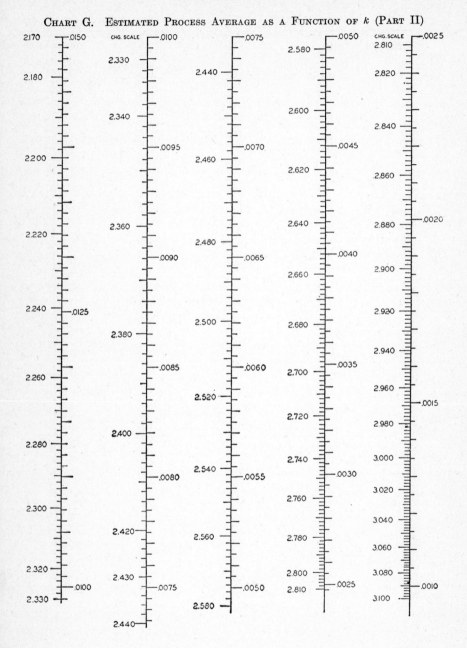

TABLE H.   UPPER AND LOWER

No. of sample items on which process average is based	Acceptable quality level														
	.024–.035		.035–.06		.06–.12		.12–.17		.17–.22		.22–.32		.32–.65		.65–1.2	
300–600	*	*	*	*	*	*	*	*	.08	.40	.11	.56	.16	1.05	.37	1.82
600–900	*	*	*	*	.03	.20	.07	.28	.10	.35	.13	.50	.19	.95	.42	1.67
900–1,200	.01	.06	.02	.10	.03	.19	.07	.26	.11	.33	.14	.47	.21	.90	.45	1.59
1,200–1,500	.01	.06	.02	.09	.04	.18	.08	.25	.11	.31	.15	.45	.22	.87	.47	1.54
1,500–2,500	.02	.05	.02	.09	.04	.17	.08	.23	.12	.30	.16	.42	.24	.83	.50	1.48
2,500–5,000	.02	.05	.03	.08	.05	.15	.09	.21	.13	.27	.17	.39	.26	.78	.54	1.40
5,000–10,000	.02	.04	.03	.07	.05	.14	.10	.20	.14	.26	.19	.37	.27	.74	.57	1.34
10,000–20,000	.02	.04	.03	.07	.05	.14	.11	.19	.15	.25	.20	.35	.29	.71	.59	1.30
20,000–40,000	.02	.04	.03	.07	.05	.13	.11	.18	.16	.23	.20	.34	.30	.69	.61	1.27
40,000–80,000	.02	.04	.03	.06	.06	.13	.11	.18	.16	.23	.21	.34	.30	.68	.62	1.25
80,000–160,000	.02	.04	.03	.06	.06	.13	.11	.18	.16	.23	.21	.33	.31	.67	.63	1.23

* More inspection results required.

Notes:

(1) If process average falls between limits, remain on normal inspection.

(2) If process average falls above upper limit for any defect, go on tightened inspection (see Chap. 5, Sec. 8).

(3) If process average falls below limits for all defects, go on reduced inspection if other criteria are met (see Chap. 5, Sec. 9).

class, in percent defective

1.2–2.2		2.2–3.2		3.2–4.4		4.4–5.3		5.3–6.4		6.4–8.5		8.5–11.0	
.73	3.14	1.45	4.39	2.21	5.84	3.15	6.91	3.88	8.19	4.77	10.80	6.43	13.85
.82	2.91	1.60	4.10	2.41	5.50	3.42	6.53	4.19	7.77	5.12	10.20	6.85	13.10
.88	2.79	1.69	3.96	2.53	5.32	3.56	6.33	4.35	7.55	5.29	9.95	7.07	12.76
.91	2.72	1.74	3.86	2.60	5.21	3.66	6.21	4.46	7.41	5.42	9.79	7.26	12.55
.96	2.62	1.82	3.74	2.70	5.06	3.78	6.04	4.60	7.23	5.61	9.52	7.52	12.30
1.02	2.50	1.92	3.59	2.83	4.88	3.95	5.84	4.79	7.00	5.87	9.18	7.79	11.90
1.07	2.41	2.00	3.47	2.94	4.74	4.08	5.68	4.93	6.82	6.03	9.02	8.01	11.67
1.11	2.35	2.06	3.39	3.01	4.64	4.17	5.57	5.04	6.70	6.15	8.85	8.17	11.44
1.14	2.30	2.10	3.34	3.07	4.57	4.24	5.49	5.12	6.61	6.25	8.67	8.33	11.22
1.15	2.27	2.13	3.30	3.11	4.52	4.28	5.43	5.17	6.55	6.28	8.62	8.39	11.14
1.17	2.25	2.15	3.27	3.13	4.48	4.32	5.39	5.21	6.50	6.30	8.58	8.42	11.10

(4) If on tightened inspection and process average falls below the upper value defining the AQL class, return to normal inspection (see Chap. 5, Sec. 8).

(5) If on reduced inspection, return to normal inspection if any one of the following occurs (see Chap. 5, Sec. 9):

(a) The process average falls above the larger value defining the AQL class.

(b) A lot is rejected.

(c) Production is interrupted.

TABLE I. SAMPLE-SIZE LETTERS FOR AVERAGE OUTGOING-QUALITY LIMIT (AOQL) CLASSES AND ACCEPTABLE QUALITY LEVEL (AQL) CLASSES

AQL class, in percent defective	AOQL class, in percent defective													
	.05–.075	.075–.10	.10–.15	.15–.22	.22–.30	.30–.50	.50–.90	.90–1.5	1.5–2.5	2.5–3.5	3.5–5.0	5.0–7.0	7.0–11.0	11.0–16.0
0.024– 0.035	O	KLMN	J											
0.035– 0.06		O	KLMN	IJ	H									
0.06 – 0.12			O	KLMN	IJ	GH								
0.12 – 0.17				O	KLMN	HIJ	FG							
0.17 – 0.22					NO	IJKLM	FGH	E						
0.22 – 0.32						LMNO	GHIJK	DEF	CDEF					
0.32 – 0.65							KLMNO	GHIJ	FGHIJ	B				
0.65 – 1.2								KLMNO	FGHIJ	B				
1.2 – 2.2									JKLMN	CDE	B			
2.2 – 3.2										FGHI	CDE	B		
3.2 – 4.4										HIJKLM	DEFG	C	B	
4.4 – 5.3											FGHIJKLM	DE	BC	
5.3 – 6.4												DEFGHIJKL	CDEF	B
6.4 – 8.5												GHIJKL	DEFGHIJK	BC
8.5 –11.0													FGHIJK	BCDE

TABLE J. FACTORS FOR CONTROL CHART LIMITS

n	$\hat{c}_2$	A	$\hat{A}_1$	$\hat{B}_3$	$\hat{B}_4$	l_1	l_2	l_3
3	0.8862	1.732	1.954	−0.3820	2.382	−0.7733	−2.618	1.471
4	0.9213	1.500	1.628	−0.1512	2.151	−1.800	−4.397	5.196
5	0.9400	1.342	1.427	−0.009253	2.009	−5.722	−10.958	38.835
6	0.9515	1.225	1.287	0.08986	1.910	17.572	27.700	290.303
7	0.9594	1.134	1.182	0.1643	1.836	4.705	6.306	17.236
8	0.9650	1.061	1.099	0.2228	1.777	3.085	3.596	6.319
9	0.9693	1.000	1.032	0.2705	1.729	2.450	2.528	3.475
10	0.9727	0.9487	0.9753	0.3103	1.690	2.111	1.954	2.287
11	0.9754	0.9045	0.9274	0.3442	1.656	1.901	1.595	1.665
12	0.9776	0.8660	0.8859	0.3736	1.626	1.758	1.348	1.291
13	0.9794	0.8320	0.8495	0.3993	1.601	1.653	1.169	1.046
14	0.9810	0.8018	0.8173	0.4221	1.578	1.574	1.032	0.8739
15	0.9823	0.7746	0.7885	0.4424	1.558	1.513	0.9239	0.7480
16	0.9835	0.7500	0.7626	0.4608	1.539	1.463	0.8365	0.6521
18	0.9854	0.7071	0.7176	0.4926	1.507	1.387	0.7039	0.5167
20	0.9869	0.6708	0.6797	0.5194	1.481	1.333	0.6078	0.4262
22	0.9882	0.6396	0.6473	0.5423	1.458	1.292	0.5349	0.3619
24	0.9892	0.6124	0.6191	0.5623	1.438	1.260	0.4777	0.3139
25	0.9896	0.6000	0.6063	0.5713	1.429	1.247	0.4535	0.2944
28	0.9908	0.5669	0.5722	0.5954	1.405	1.213	0.3936	0.2476
30	0.9914	0.5477	0.5525	0.6093	1.391	1.196	0.3618	0.2238
32	0.9920	0.5303	0.5346	0.6220	1.378	1.181	0.3348	0.2040
35	0.9927	0.5071	0.5108	0.6388	1.361	1.162	0.3011	0.1801
36	0.9929	0.5000	0.5036	0.6439	1.356	1.157	0.2913	0.1733
40	0.9936	0.4743	0.4774	0.6624	1.338	1.139	0.2578	0.1505
45	0.9943	0.4472	0.4498	0.6820	1.318	1.121	0.2255	0.1293
50	0.9949	0.4243	0.4264	0.6985	1.302	1.107	0.2003	0.1132
55	0.9954	0.4045	0.4064	0.7126	1.287	1.096	0.1802	0.1006
60	0.9958	0.3873	0.3889	0.7250	1.275	1.088	0.1638	0.09059
70	0.9964	0.3586	0.3599	0.7455	1.254	1.074	0.1386	0.07547
85	0.9970	0.3254	0.3264	0.7692	1.231	1.060	0.1126	0.06037
100	0.9975	0.3000	0.3008	0.7873	1.213	1.050	0.09477	0.05025
125	0.9980	0.2683	0.2689	0.8099	1.190	1.040	0.07502	0.03934
200	0.9987	0.2121	0.2124	0.8498	1.150	1.024	0.04616	0.02371

TABLE K. SUMMARY OF SINGLE-SAMPLING VARIABLES PLANS FOR KNOWN SIGMA, CLASSIFIED BY ACCEPTABLE QUALITY LEVEL AND SAMPLE-SIZE LETTER

Values of k' for acceptance criteria of the form $\bar{x} + k'\sigma \leq U$ or $\bar{x} - k'\sigma \geq L$

Sample-size letter	Single-sample size	Acceptable quality level class, in percent defective														
		.024–.035	.035–.06	.06–.12	.12–.17	.17–.22	.22–.32	.32–.65	.65–1.20	1.20–2.20	2.20–3.20	3.20–4.40	4.40–5.30	5.30–6.40	6.40–8.50	8.50–11.00
B	5	↓	↓	↓	↓	↓	↓	1.748	1.522	1.278	1.117	1.027	1.015	0.786	0.669	0.546
C	6	↓	↓	↓	↓	↓	↓	1.812	1.586	1.343	1.272	1.181	0.973	0.936	0.851	0.701
D	7	↓	↓	↓	↓	↓	2.105	1.862	1.635	1.432	1.392	1.177	1.084	0.933	0.854	0.751
E	9	↓	↓	↓	↓	2.300	2.178	1.935	1.709	1.466	1.363	1.226	1.158	1.006	0.928	0.824
F	11	↓	↓	↓	2.433	2.352	2.231	1.988	1.761	1.518	1.400	1.356	1.210	1.093	0.980	0.876
G	13	↓	↓	2.579	2.473	2.392	2.270	2.028	1.801	1.558	1.539	1.396	1.250	1.160	1.020	0.916
H	16	↓	2.828	2.624	2.518	2.437	2.315	2.073	1.846	1.664	1.532	1.351	1.253	1.178	1.065	0.961
I	20	↓	2.871	2.668	2.561	2.480	2.359	2.116	1.889	1.646	1.528	1.407	1.328	1.249	1.154	1.004
J	24	3.054	2.903	2.700	2.593	2.512	2.391	2.148	1.921	1.718	1.560	1.451	1.329	1.281	1.186	1.036
K	28	3.079	2.928	2.725	2.618	2.537	2.416	2.173	1.980	1.764	1.616	1.501	1.395	1.306	1.211	1.061
L	32	3.099	2.948	2.745	2.638	2.557	2.436	2.193	1.966	1.806	1.636	1.521	1.415	1.290	↑	↑
M	36	3.115	2.965	2.762	2.655	2.574	2.452	2.238	2.052	1.834	1.653	1.525	↑	↑	↑	↑
N	40	3.130	2.979	2.776	2.669	2.588	2.466	2.252	2.106	1.837	↑	↑	↑	↑	↑	↑
O	45	3.144	2.994	2.845	2.723	2.649	2.514	2.331	2.120	↑	↑	↑	↑	↑	↑	↑

Notes:
↓ Use the first sampling plan below arrow. If sample size is larger than inspection-lot size, use 100 percent inspection or form larger inspection lots.
↑ Use the first sampling plan above arrow.

TABLE L. SUMMARY OF DOUBLE-SAMPLE VARIABLES PLANS FOR KNOWN SIGMA, CLASSIFIED BY ACCEPTABLE QUALITY LEVEL AND SAMPLE-SIZE LETTER

Sample-size letter	Sample	Sample size	Combined sample size	Constant	Acceptable quality level class, in percent defective														
					.024–.035	.035–.06	.06–.12	.12–.17	.17–.22	.22–.32	.32–.65	.65–1.2	1.2–2.2	2.2–3.2	3.2–4.4	4.4–5.3	5.3–6.4	6.4–8.5	8.5–11.0
D*	First	3	3	k'_a						2.61	2.37	2.14	1.94	1.90	1.68	1.59	1.44	1.36	1.26
	Second	6	9	k'_r	→	→	→	→	→	1.67	1.43	1.20	1.00	0.96	0.75	0.66	0.51	0.43	0.33
				k'_t						2.07	1.83	1.60	1.40	1.36	1.15	1.05	0.90	0.82	0.72
E	First	4	4	k'_a					2.71	2.59	2.35	2.12	1.88	1.78	1.64	1.57	1.42	1.34	1.24
	Second	8	12	k'_r	→	→	→	→	1.94	1.82	1.57	1.35	1.10	1.00	0.86	0.80	0.64	0.57	0.47
				k'_t					2.26	2.14	1.90	1.67	1.43	1.33	1.19	1.12	0.97	0.89	0.79
F	First	5	5	k'_a				2.79	2.71	2.59	2.35	2.12	1.88	1.76	1.72	1.57	1.45	1.34	1.23
	Second	10	15	k'_r	→	→	→	2.14	2.05	1.93	1.69	1.46	1.22	1.10	1.06	0.91	0.79	0.68	0.58
				k'_t				2.40	2.32	2.19	1.95	1.73	1.48	1.37	1.32	1.18	1.06	0.95	0.85
G	First	6	6	k'_a			2.91	2.80	2.72	2.60	2.36	2.13	1.89	1.87	1.73	1.58	1.49	1.35	1.24
	Second	12	18	k'_r	→	→	2.31	2.20	2.12	2.00	1.76	1.53	1.29	1.27	1.13	0.98	0.89	0.75	0.65
				k'_t			2.54	2.44	2.36	2.23	2.00	1.77	1.52	1.50	1.36	1.21	1.13	0.99	0.89
H	First	8	8	k'_a		3.06	2.86	2.75	2.67	2.55	2.31	2.08	1.90	1.77	1.59	1.49	1.41	1.30	1.19
	Second	16	24	k'_r	→	2.63	2.43	2.31	2.23	2.11	1.87	1.64	1.46	1.33	1.15	1.05	0.97	0.86	0.76
				k'_t		2.80	2.59	2.49	2.40	2.28	2.04	1.81	1.63	1.50	1.32	1.22	1.15	1.03	0.93
I	First	10	10	k'_a		3.08	2.88	2.77	2.69	2.57	2.33	2.10	1.86	1.74	1.62	1.54	1.46	1.36	1.21
	Second	20	30	k'_r	→	2.69	2.49	2.38	2.31	2.18	1.94	1.71	1.47	1.35	1.23	1.15	1.07	0.98	0.83
				k'_t		2.84	2.64	2.53	2.45	2.33	2.09	1.86	1.62	1.50	1.38	1.30	1.22	1.13	0.98

J	First	12	24	k'_a	3.25	3.10	2.90	2.79	2.72	2.59	2.35	2.12	1.92	1.76	1.65	1.53	1.48	1.38	1.24
	Second	12	36	k'_r	2.90	2.74	2.54	2.43	2.35	2.23	1.99	1.76	1.56	1.40	1.29	1.17	1.12	1.03	0.88
				k'_t	3.03	2.87	2.67	2.56	2.48	2.36	2.12	1.89	1.69	1.53	1.42	1.30	1.25	1.16	1.01
K	First	14	28	k'_a	3.26	3.10	2.91	2.80	2.72	2.60	2.35	2.16	1.94	1.80	1.68	1.58	1.49	1.39	1.24
	Second	14	42	k'_r	2.93	2.79	2.58	2.47	2.39	2.27	2.02	1.83	1.61	1.47	1.35	1.25	1.16	1.06	0.91
				k'_t	3.05	2.90	2.70	2.59	2.51	2.39	2.15	1.95	1.74	1.59	1.48	1.37	1.28	1.19	1.04
L	First	16	32	k'_a	3.27	3.12	2.90	2.80	2.71	2.59	2.35	2.12	1.96	1.79	1.68	1.57	1.44	←	←
	Second	16	48	k'_r	2.95	2.80	2.60	2.50	2.42	2.30	2.05	1.83	1.67	1.50	1.38	1.28	1.15		
				k'_t	3.08	2.93	2.73	2.62	2.54	2.42	2.17	1.95	1.79	1.62	1.50	1.40	1.27		
M	First	18	36	k'_a	3.25	3.12	2.93	2.81	2.73	2.61	2.38	2.21	1.99	1.81	1.68	←	←	←	←
	Second	18	54	k'_r	2.99	2.83	2.63	2.52	2.44	2.32	2.11	1.92	1.70	1.52	1.39				
				k'_t	3.09	2.94	2.74	2.64	2.56	2.43	2.22	2.03	1.82	1.63	1.51				
N	First	20	40	k'_a	3.28	3.11	2.92	2.82	2.74	2.61	2.40	2.25	1.98	←	←	←	←	←	←
	Second	20	60	k'_r	3.00	2.85	2.65	2.55	2.47	2.34	2.13	1.98	1.71						
				k'_t	3.11	2.96	2.76	2.65	2.57	2.45	2.23	2.09	1.82						
O	First	22	44	k'_a	3.27	3.13	2.98	2.85	2.78	2.65	2.47	2.26	←	←	←	←	←	←	←
	Second	22	66	k'_r	3.02	2.86	2.71	2.59	2.52	2.38	2.20	1.99							
				k'_t	3.13	2.99	2.84	2.72	2.64	2.51	2.32	2.11							

Notes:

* Known-sigma double-sampling variables plans for sample-size letters B and C are not given because their use results in no saving over the corresponding single-sampling plans. If sample size is larger than inspection-lot size, use 100 percent inspection or form larger inspection lots.

↓ Use the first sampling plan below arrow.

↑ Use the first sampling plan above arrow.

TABLE M. COMPARISON OF AQL AND LTPD FOR

Sample-size letter	Single-sample size Un-known σ	Single-sample size Known σ		.024–.035 Un-known σ	.024–.035 Known σ	.035–.06 Un-known σ	.035–.06 Known σ	.06–.12 Un-known σ	.06–.12 Known σ	.12–.17 Un-known σ	.12–.17 Known σ	.17–.22 Un-known σ	.17–.22 Known σ	.22–.32 Un-known σ	.22–.32 Known σ
B	7	5	AQL												
			LTPD												
C	10	6	AQL												
			LTPD												
D	13	7	AQL											0.32	0.32
			LTPD											9.61	5.26
E	16	9	AQL									0.22	0.22	0.32	0.32
			LTPD									6.68	3.06	7.74	4.00
F	20	11	AQL							0.17	0.17	0.22	0.22	0.32	0.32
			LTPD							4.68	2.03	5.24	2.47	6.17	3.26
G	25	13	AQL					0.12	0.12	0.17	0.17	0.22	0.22	0.32	0.32
			LTPD					3.11	1.31	3.67	1.71	4.14	2.09	4.96	2.78
H	35	16	AQL			0.06	0.06	0.12	0.12	0.17	0.17	0.22	0.22	0.30	0.32
			LTPD			1.49	0.61	2.15	1.06	2.58	1.40	2.97	1.72	3.50	2.30
I	50	20	AQL			0.06	0.06	0.12	0.12	0.17	0.17	0.22	0.22	0.32	0.32
			LTPD			1.00	0.49	1.49	0.86	1.83	1.15	2.14	1.41	2.67	1.91
J	60	24	AQL	0.035	0.035	0.06	0.06	0.12	0.12	0.17	0.17	0.22	0.22	0.32	0.32
			LTPD	0.59	0.26	0.82	0.41	1.26	0.74	1.56	0.99	1.83	1.22	2.31	1.66
K	70	28	AQL	0.035	0.035	0.06	0.06	0.12	0.12	0.17	0.17	0.22	0.22	0.32	0.32
			LTPD	0.50	0.23	0.70	0.36	1 09	0.65	1.37	0.88	1.61	1.09	2.05	1.49
L	85	32	AQL	0.035	0.035	0.06	0.06	0.12	0.12	0.17	0.17	0.22	0.22	0.32	0.32
			LTPD	0.41	0.20	0.58	0.32	0.93	0.59	1 17	0.79	1.39	0.99	1.78	1.36
M	100	36	AQL	0.035	0.035	0.06	0.06	0.11	0.12	0.17	0.17	0.21	0.22	0.30	0.32
			LTPD	0.35	0.19	0.50	0.30	0.76	0.54	1.03	0.73	1 19	0.91	1 52	1.26
N	125	40	AQL	0.035	0.035	0.06	0.06	0 11	0.12	0.17	0.17	0.20	0.22	0.30	0.32
			LTPD	0.28	0.17	0.42	0.28	0.64	0.50	0.88	0 68	0.99	0.85	1.32	1.18
O	200	45	AQL	0.035	0.035	0.06	0.06	0 10	0.10	0.14	0.15	0.19	0.19	0.29	0.29
			LTPD	0.19	0.16	0.29	0 25	0.43	0.40	0.56	0.57	0.71	0.70	0.98	1.01

TABLE N. UPPER AND LOWER LIMITS ON

No. of sample items on which process average is based	.024–.035		.035–.06		.06–.12		.12–.17		.17–.22		.22–.32		.32–.65		.65–1.20	
100–150	*	*	*	*	*	*	*	*	.10	.38	.13	.54	.19	1.05	.39	1.87
150–200	*	*	*	*	*	*	*	*	.10	.35	.14	.50	.20	.98	.42	1.75
200–300	*	*	*	*	*	*	*	*	.11	.32	.15	.46	.22	.91	.46	1.65
300–400	.016	.051	.024	.09	.04	.17	.08	.24	.12	.30	.16	.44	.23	.87	.48	1.57
400–500	.017	.049	.025	.08	.04	.16	.09	.23	.13	.29	.16	.42	.24	.84	.50	1.52
500–700	.018	.047	.026	.08	.05	.16	.09	.22	.13	.28	.17	.41	.25	.81	.52	1.47
700–1,000	.019	.045	.027	.08	.05	.15	.10	.21	.14	.27	.18	.39	.26	.78	.54	1.43
1,000–1,500	.019	.043	.029	.07	.05	.14	.10	.20	.14	.26	.18	.38	.27	.76	.56	1.38
1,500–2,000	.020	.041	.029	.07	.05	.14	.10	.20	.15	.25	.19	.37	.28	.74	.57	1.35
2,000–3,000	.021	.040	.030	.07	.05	.14	.11	.19	.15	.25	.19	.36	.28	.72	.58	1.33
3,000–5,000	.021	.039	.031	.07	.05	.13	.11	.19	.15	.24	.20	.35	.29	.71	.60	1.30
5,000–10,000	.022	.038	.032	.07	.06	.13	.11	.18	.16	.24	.20	.34	.30	.69	.61	1.27
10,000–20,000	.023	.037	.033	.06	.06	.13	.11	.18	.16	.23	.21	.34	.30	.68	.62	1.25

* More inspection results required.

SINGLE-SAMPLING KNOWN-SIGMA AND UNKNOWN-SIGMA PLANS

Acceptable quality level class, in percent defective

32–.65		.65–1.2		1.2–2.2		2.2–3.2		3.2–4.4		4.4–5.3		5.3–6.4		6.4–8.5		8.5–11.0	
Un-known	Known	Un-known	Known	Un-known	Known	Un-known	Known	Un-known	Known	Un-known	Known	Un-known	Known	Un-known	Known	Un-known	Known
σ	σ	σ	σ	σ	σ	σ	σ	σ	σ	σ	σ	σ	σ	σ	σ	σ	σ
0.50	0.65	1.00	1.20	2.00	2.20	3.00	3.20	3.50	3.90	4.40	4.00	6.40	6.40	8.50	8.00	10.50	10.00
20.73	12.00	24.68	17.15	29.57	24.03	33.05	29.34	34.52	32.50	36.89	32.93	41.24	41.55	45.10	46.16	48.32	51.08
0.50	0.65	1.00	1.20	1 70	2.20	2.20	2.60	3.20	3.20	5.30	5.00	5.60	5.40	8.50	6.40	10.50	·8.50
14.60	9.87	18.18	14.40	21.62	20.63	24.26	22.71	26.78	25.54	32.02	32.63	32.67	34.00	38.19	37.17	41.47	42.96
0.65	0.65	1.20	1.20	1.70	2.00	2.30	2.20	3.80	3.60	4.40	4.40	6.40	6.00	7.20	7.00	10.00	8.50
12.42	8.41	15.57	12.49	17.76	17.16	19.94	18.19	24.29	24.41	25.76	27.43	30.04	32.68	31.56	35.58	36.35	39.51
0.65	0.65	1.00	1.20	2.20	2.20	2.60	2.80	4.00	3.80	4.40	4.40	5.90	6.00	8.30	7.00	10.00	8.50
10.28	6.57	12.25	10.00	17.01	14.95	18.26	17.47	22.00	21.22	22.94	23.25	26.14	28.12	30.55	30.84	33.33	34.58
0.65	0.65	1.00	1.20	2.10	2.20	2.90	2.90	3.20	3.20	4.50	4.40	6.10	5.60	7.50	7.00	9.50	8.50
8.44	5.46	10.23	8.46	14.35	12.89	16.68	15.54	17 47	16.61	20.55	20.51	23.81	23.98	26.36	27.64	29.68	31.21
0.65	0.65	1.15	1.20	2.00	2.20	2.40	2.30	3.30	3.20	4.50	4.40	5.70	5.30	7.80	7.00	9.50	8.50
6.97	4.72	9.21	7.42	12.12	11.46	13.28	11.83	15.61	14.90	18.31	18.56	20.70	21.05	24.44	25.33	27.18	28.76
0.60	0.65	1.20	1.20	1.80	1.90	2.50	2.60	3.80	3.90	4.90	4.80	6.40	5.60	7.90	7.00	9.00	8.50
5.09	3.99	7.42	6.36	9.28	8.96	11.15	11.28	14.11	15.13	16.31	17.54	18.33	19.55	21.52	22.84	23.24	26.09
0.65	0.65	1.20	1.20	2.10	2.20	2.90	2.90	4.00	3.80	5.00	4.50	5.70	5.30	7.60	6.40	8.80	8.50
4.07	3.37	5.89	5.45	8.27	8.70	10.08	10.72	12.31	13.13	14.15	14.89	15.36	16.80	18.43	19.28	20 24	23.64
0.65	0.65	1.20	1.20	2.00	2.00	3.00	2.90	4.10	3.70	5.10	4.80	6.00	5.30	7.80	6.40	8.80	8.50
3.59	2.96	5.27	4.85	7.29	7.26	9.45	9.71	11.56	11.72	13.32	14.29	14.82	15.41	17.61	17.76	19.08	21.92
0.65	0.65	1.10	1.10	1.90	1.90	2.80	2.70	3.90	3.50	4.90	4.40	6.10	5.30	7.70	6.40	8.80	8.50
3.24	2.68	4.56	4.12	6.52	6.40	8.42	8.48	10.50	10.40	12.23	12.45	14.18	14.38	16.61	16.63	18.20	20.63
0.63	0.65	1.10	1.20	1.80	1.80	2.80	2.70	3.80	3.50	4.80	4.40	6.20	5.70				
2.81	2.46	4.09	4.09	5.72	5.71	7.74	7.93	9.56	9.77	11.24	11.73	13.44	14.39				
0.55	0.60	1.00	1.00	1.75	1.75	2.70	2.70	3.60	3.60								
2.32	2.15	3.51	3.30	5.20	5.25	7.06	7.51	8.66	9.49								
0.55	0.60	0.90	0.90	1.80	1.80												
2.04	2.02	2.91	2.85	4.81	5.11												
0.50	0.50	0.90	0.90														
1.49	1.62	2.34	2.68														

PROCESS AVERAGE FOR KNOWN-SIGMA PLANS

class, in percent defective

1.20–2.20		2.20–3.20		3.20–4.40		4.40–5.30		5.30–6.40		6.40–8.50		8.50–11.00	
.75	3.30	1.43	4.68	2.13	6.29	3.00	7.48	3.66	8.90	4.48	11.57	6.09	14.66
.81	3.10	1.53	4.42	2.27	5.96	3.19	7.10	3.88	8.47	4.74	11.05	6.42	14.04
.86	2.94	1.63	4.20	2.41	5.68	3.36	6.78	4.09	8.10	4.99	10.60	6.73	13.51
.91	2.81	1.71	4.03	2.52	5.47	3.51	6.53	4.26	7.82	5.19	10.25	6.98	13.10
.94	2.73	1.76	3.92	2.59	5.33	3.61	6.37	4.37	7.64	5.32	10.03	7.15	12.84
.97	2.65	1.81	3.82	2.67	5.20	3.70	6.22	4.49	7.46	5.46	9.81	7.32	12.58
1.01	2.58	1.87	3.71	2.75	5.06	3.81	6.07	4.61	7.29	5.60	9.59	7.50	12.32
1.04	2.51	1.92	3.62	2.82	4.94	3.91	5.93	4.73	7.12	5.73	9.40	7.67	12.08
1.06	2.46	1.97	3.54	2.88	4.85	3.98	5.83	4.81	7.01	5.83	9.25	7.79	11.91
1.08	2.41	2.00	3.49	2.93	4.78	4.05	5.74	4.89	6.91	5.92	9.13	7.91	11.75
1.11	2.37	2.04	3.43	2.98	4.70	4.12	5.64	4.97	6.80	6.02	8.99	8.03	11.59
1.13	2.32	2.08	3.37	3.04	4.61	4.19	5.55	5.06	6.69	6.12	8.86	8.15	11.43
1.15	2.29	2.12	3.32	3.09	4.55	4.25	5.48	5.13	6.60	6.20	8.75	8.25	11.30

Chart O. Nomograph to Determine $P(A_2)$

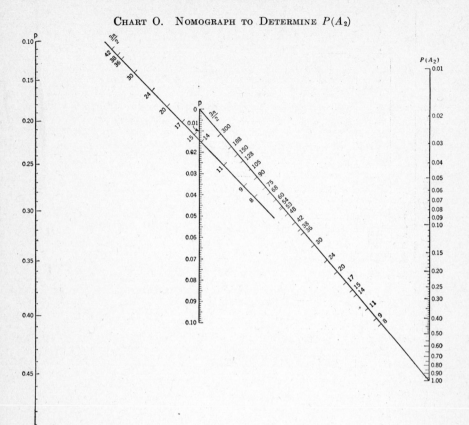

TABLE P. TABLE OF POINTS FOR CONSTRUCTING ACCEPTANCE REGIONS FOR TWO-SIDED SPECIFICATION LIMITS

Acceptable quality level class, in percent defective

Sample-size letter	Abscissa	.024–.035	.035–.06	.06–.12	.12–.17	.17–.22	.22–.32	.32–.65	.65–1.2	1.2–2.2	2.2–3.2	3.2–4.4	4.4–5.3	5.3–6.4	6.4–8.5	8.5–11.0
B	0							.557	.602	.661	.705	.724	.756	.819	.879	.934
	.025							.556	.601	.661	.705	.724	.756	.819	.879	.934
	.05							.553	.599	.659	.703	.723	.755	.818	.878	.933
	.075							.548	.596	.657	.701	.721	.753	.816	.877	.932
	.1							.541	.591	.653	.698	.718	.750	.814	.875	.930
	.15							.519	.576	.642	.689	.709	.743	.808	.869	.925
	.2							.489	.551	.625	.676	.697	.731	.798	.861	.918
	.3								.483	.564	.653	.653	.694	.768	.835	.895
	.4										.542	.570	.619	.714	.793	.858
	.5													.609	.714	.798
	.6														.575	.672
C	0							.512	.556	.598	.631	.663	.734	.743	.824	.876
	.025							.512	.556	.598	.631	.663	.733	.742	.823	.876
	.05							.509	.554	.596	.629	.662	.732	.741	.822	.875
	.075							.505	.550	.593	.627	.659	.730	.739	.821	.873
	.1							.498	.545	.589	.623	.656	.727	.736	.818	.871
	.15							.480	.530	.576	.612	.645	.718	.728	.811	.865
	.2							.455	.508	.557	.595	.630	.706	.716	.801	.855
	.3							.399	.448	.500	.542	.582	.666	.677	.769	.827
	.4										.466	.506	.599	.612	.717	.781
	.5												.503	.515	.630	.706
	.6														.507	.582
D	0						.466	.503	.544	.572	.599	.656	.676	.734	.756	.828
	.025						.465	.502	.543	.571	.599	.655	.675	.734	.755	.827
	.05						.462	.500	.541	.569	.597	.654	.674	.733	.754	.826
	.075						.457	.496	.538	.566	.594	.651	.671	.730	.752	.825
	.1						.451	.491	.533	.562	.590	.648	.668	.727	.749	.822
	.15						.432	.474	.519	.549	.578	.638	.658	.719	.741	.815
	.2						.409	.452	.499	.530	.561	.623	.644	.706	.729	.804
	.3							.397	.442	.475	.508	.576	.599	.667	.692	.772
	.4									.408	.438	.504	.529	.604	.631	.720
	.5											.421	.442	.511	.539	.638
	.6														.432	.518
E	0					.434	.451	.487	.514	.577	.593	.643	.655	.699	.762	.804
	.025					.433	.450	.486	.513	.576	.593	.642	.655	.698	.761	.803
	.05					.430	.447	.484	.511	.575	.591	.641	.653	.697	.760	.802
	.075					.425	.443	.480	.508	.572	.588	.638	.651	.695	.758	.800
	.1					.419	.436	.475	.503	.567	.584	.635	.647	.692	.755	.798

F

abscissa											
.15	.790	.747	.682	.637	.624	.572	.555	.488	.459	.418	.400
.2	.779	.735	.669	.622	.609	.556	.537	.468	.437	.396	.378
.3	.745	.699	.627	.577	.562	.504	.485	.413	.384	.347	
.4	.691	.639	.561	.508	.492	.435	.418				
.5	.606	.551	.472	.424	.411						
.6	.491	.442									

G

abscissa													
0	.769	.749	.656	.623	.586	.554	.537	.495	.460	.425	.410	.400	.387
.025	.768	.748	.656	.622	.585	.553	.536	.494	.459	.424	.408	.399	.386
.05	.767	.747	.654	.621	.583	.551	.534	.492	.457	.422	.406	.396	.383
.075	.765	.745	.652	.618	.581	.548	.531	.488	.453	.417	.401	.391	.378
.1	.763	.743	.648	.615	.577	.544	.527	.484	.447	.411	.395	.384	.372
.15	.754	.734	.638	.604	.565	.531	.514	.469	.432	.395	.378	.367	.354
.2	.742	.722	.624	.589	.549	.514	.496	.450	.411	.374	.357	.347	.334
.3	.706	.684	.580	.542	.500	.463	.445	.399	.362	.328			
.4	.649	.625	.514	.475	.433	.399	.382						
.5	.562	.539	.430	.396	.361								
.6	.452	.433	.344										
.7		.325											

H

abscissa														
0	.713	.688	.642	.613	.580	.538	.510	.481	.440	.407	.395	.386	.374	.353
.025	.712	.687	.641	.613	.580	.538	.510	.480	.439	.407	.394	.385	.373	.352
.05	.711	.686	.640	.611	.579	.536	.508	.478	.437	.404	.391	.382	.370	.349
.075	.709	.684	.637	.608	.577	.533	.504	.474	.433	.400	.387	.377	.365	.343
.1	.706	.680	.634	.605	.573	.531	.500	.469	.427	.394	.381	.371	.359	.337
.15	.697	.671	.624	.594	.561	.516	.487	.455	.412	.378	.365	.354	.342	.320
.2	.684	.657	.609	.579	.545	.499	.468	.436	.392	.358	.345	.335	.322	.301
.3	.644	.616	.565	.532	.497	.449	.418	.386	.344	.313	.302	.293	.282	
.4	.583	.553	.499	.466	.431	.386	.359	.331	.295	.269				
.5	.497	.468	.418	.389	.360	.322	.299							
.6	.398	.375	.335	.312	.288									
.7	.299	.281												

(Table P is continued on the following page.)

Notes:

(1) On the horizontal axis (abscissa) mark off from −1 through 0 to +1 by tenths.   (A suggested scale is ½ inch for each 0.1 unit.)

(2) Plot each ordinate for both a positive and negative absissa value.

(3) Connect each end of the curve obtained by step (2) with the corresponding end-points of the horizontal axis; that is, at −1 and +1 on the horizontal axis.

TABLE P. TABLE OF POINTS FOR CONSTRUCTING ACCEPTANCE REGIONS FOR TWO-SIDED SPECIFICATION LIMITS—(Continued)

Sample-size letter	Abscissa	Acceptable quality level class, in percent defective														
		.024–.035	.035–.06	.06–.12	.12–.17	.17–.22	.22–.32	.32–.65	.65–1.2	1.2–2.2	2.2–3.2	3.2–4.4	4.4–5.3	5.3–6.4	6.4–8.5	8.5–11.0
I	0		.342	.362	.374	.383	.398	.431	.466	.507	.536	.570	.597	.615	.660	.687
	.025		.341	.361	.372	.381	.397	.430	.465	.507	.535	.570	.597	.615	.660	.687
	.05		.338	.358	.370	.379	.394	.427	.463	.505	.534	.568	.595	.613	.659	.685
	.075		.333	.354	.365	.375	.390	.423	.460	.501	.531	.565	.593	.611	.656	.683
	.1		.326	.347	.359	.369	.384	.418	.455	.497	.526	.561	.589	.607	.653	.680
	.15		.310	.331	.343	.353	.368	.403	.441	.484	.514	.549	.578	.596	.643	.670
	.2		.292	.313	.324	.334	.349	.384	.422	.466	.497	.533	.562	.581	.629	.657
	.3					.292	.306	.337	.373	.416	.448	.485	.516	.535	.586	.616
	.4								.320	.358	.386	.421	.450	.470	.522	.553
	.5											.351	.376	.393	.440	.469
	.6															.375
J	0	.324	.337	.357	.368	.378	.392	.425	.460	.497	.532	.565	.592	.614	.656	.677
	.025	.323	.336	.356	.368	.377	.391	.424	.459	.496	.531	.565	.591	.614	.655	.677
	.05	.319	.333	.353	.365	.374	.389	.422	.457	.494	.530	.563	.590	.612	.654	.676
	.075	.314	.328	.349	.360	.370	.384	.418	.453	.491	.527	.560	.587	.610	.651	.674
	.1	.308	.322	.342	.354	.364	.379	.412	.449	.486	.522	.556	.583	.606	.648	.671
	.15	.292	.306	.326	.338	.348	.363	.397	.434	.473	.510	.545	.572	.595	.638	.661
	.2	.275	.288	.308	.320	.329	.344	.378	.415	.454	.493	.528	.556	.580	.624	.647
	.3				.280	.288	.301	.332	.367	.405	.444	.480	.510	.534	.581	.606
	.4								.315	.348	.383	.417	.445	.469	.517	.542
	.5											.347	.372	.393	.435	.459
	.6														.348	.368
K	0	.320	.334	.353	.365	.374	.388	.420	.449	.487	.520	.554	.581	.610	.647	.671
	.025	.319	.332	.352	.364	.373	.387	.419	.449	.486	.519	.552	.580	.610	.646	.670
	.05	.316	.329	.349	.361	.370	.384	.417	.447	.485	.518	.550	.578	.608	.645	.668
	.075	.311	.325	.345	.356	.366	.380	.413	.443	.481	.515	.548	.576	.606	.642	.666
	.1	.304	.318	.339	.350	.360	.374	.408	.438	.476	.510	.544	.572	.602	.639	.663
	.15	.289	.303	.323	.334	.344	.359	.393	.424	.463	.498	.532	.560	.591	.629	.654
	.2		.285	.305	.316	.326	.340	.373	.405	.445	.480	.516	.544	.576	.615	.640
	.3				.277	.285	.298	.328	.358	.396	.431	.467	.497	.530	.571	.597
	.4									.340	.371	.405	.433	.465	.507	.534
	.5												.362	.390	.426	.452
	.6														.341	.362
L	0	.316	.329	.349	.360	.369	.383	.413	.444	.477	.514	.544	.571	.605		.671
	.025	.315	.328	.348	.359	.368	.382	.412	.443	.477	.513	.544	.570	.604		.670
	.05	.312	.325	.345	.356	.365	.380	.410	.441	.475	.511	.542	.569	.603		.668
	.075	.307	.320	.340	.352	.361	.376	.406	.437	.471	.508	.539	.566	.600		.666
	.1	.301	.314	.334	.346	.355	.370	.401	.432	.466	.504	.535	.562	.597		.663

Curve	x	1	2	3	4	5	6	7	8	9	10	11	12	13
M	.15	.285	.299	.319	.330	.340	.354	.386	.418	.453	.491	.523	.551	.586
	.2	.269	.282	.301	.312	.321	.336	.367	.399	.435	.473	.506	.534	.570
	.3					.281	.294	.322	.352	.386	.425	.458	.487	.525
	.4								.302	.332	.366	.396	.423	.460
	.5											.330	.353	.385
N	0	.313	.326	.343	.357	.364	.377	.403	.434	.471	.506	.533		
	.025	.312	.325	.342	.356	.363	.376	.402	.433	.470	.505	.533		
	.05	.309	.322	.339	.353	.360	.373	.400	.431	.468	.503	.531		
	.075	.304	.317	.334	.348	.356	.369	.396	.427	.464	.500	.528		
	.1	.298	.311	.328	.342	.350	.364	.390	.422	.460	.496	.524		
	.15	.282	.296	.313	.327	.334	.348	.375	.408	.446	.483	.512		
	.2	.266	.279	.295	.309	.316	.329	.356	.389	.427	.465	.495		
	.3				.270	.277	.289	.313	.343	.380	.416	.446		
	.4									.326	.358	.385		
	.5										.299	.321		
O	0	.303	.315	.329	.339	.348	.363	.385	.397	.414	.422	.466		
	.025	.302	.314	.328	.338	.347	.362	.384	.397	.413	.422	.466		
	.05	.299	.311	.325	.335	.345	.360	.382	.394	.411	.419	.464		
	.075	.294	.307	.321	.331	.340	.356	.378	.390	.407	.416	.460		
	.1	.288	.301	.315	.325	.335	.350	.373	.385	.402	.411	.456		
	.15	.273	.286	.300	.310	.320	.335	.358	.371	.388	.397	.442		
	.2		.269	.283	.292	.302	.317	.340	.352	.369	.378	.424		
	.3							.298	.309	.325	.333	.377		
	.4									.278	.285	.323		

Notes:

(1) On the horizontal axis (abscissa) mark off from −1 through 0 to +1 by tenths. (A suggested scale is ⅔ inch for each 0.1 unit.)

(2) Plot each ordinate for both a positive and negative abscissa value.

(3) Connect each end of the curve obtained by step (2) with the corresponding end-points of the horizontal axis; that is, at −1 and +1 on the horizontal axis.

INDEX

A

Acceptable quality level (AQL), as basis for classification of plans, 27–28, 116
  change of, 39, 43, 64, 66
  definition of, 27–28, 41, 50
  in reduced inspection, 67
  selection of, 41–43, 64, 84–87, 93, 100
  table of, for variables plans, 169
  in tightened inspection, 39, 66
Acceptable quality level class, 50, 66, 68
Acceptable quality level range, 28, 41
Acceptance (*see* Inspection lot, acceptance of)
Acceptance criteria, choice of forms, 59–60
  for classified defects, 41
  combined plans, 70, 140
  difference method, 150–151
  in double sampling, 17–18, 57–59, **78**, 95–96, 127–128, 150
  graphical forms, 60, 83–84, 153–155, 156
  for known-sigma plans, 78, 125, 127
  for one-sided limit, 16–18, 55–59, **77**, 146
  optional forms, 59–60, 148–150
    table of constants for, 190–191
  quadratic method, 151–155
  in single sampling, 16–17, 55–56, **78**, 89–91, 125–127, 146, 149–150
  squared-difference method, 155–156
  for two-sided limits, 80–81, 83–85, 134–140
Acceptance inspection, 1
  administration of, 6, **7**, 32, 41, 51, 115
  costs of, 5, 6, 9, 32, 36–39, 46, 100
  methods of, 9–10
  objectives of, 9, 10, 42, 99, 100
  use of control charts in, 5, 9–10, 74–75, 99–103
Acceptance number, 70

Acceptance region, 84, 154
Acceptance sampling (*see* Acceptance inspection; Sampling inspection)
American Machinist, 72n.
American Standards Association, 98*n.*
Amount of inspection, 43–44
  in combined plans, 21, 70
  in double sampling, 33–36, 48, 121–122
  in reduced inspection, 67
  in sampling inspection by variables, 4–5, 32–33
  savings in, through double-sampling plans, 33, 36
    through known-sigma plans, 73–74, 76
    through sampling inspection by variables, 4–5, 32–33, 36
  in sequential sampling by attributes, 35–36, 48
  in single sampling, 33–36
  (*See also* Sample size; Sample-size letter)
Annals of Mathematical Statistics, The, 127*n.*, 136*n.*, 137*n.*
Army Service Forces, 121
Arnold, K. J., 136
Attribute sampling inspection, 1, 6–7, 32, 114, 121
Average outgoing quality (AOQ), 30–31, 68
  maximum, 31, 68–69
Average outgoing-quality limit (AOQL), 31, 68–69
Average sample number (ASN), 35–36

B

Bell System Technical Journal, 7n.
Bell Telephone Laboratories, 7
Biometrika, 126*n.*
Blackwell, David, 137*n.*
Borderline items, 5, 145

C

Calculating machine, use of, 55, 143, 148
Calculations, 54
  for difference method, 150
  for double-sampling plans, 47, 56–59,
    96
  for known-sigma plans, 78
  for optional form of standard criteria,
    148–150
  for quadratic method, 151–153
  simplification of, 143–148, 152
  for single-sampling plans, 54–56, 89
  squared-difference method, 155–156
Circumflex, use of, 105n.
Class intervals, 21–22
Classification, of defectives, 41
  of sampling plans, 27–28, 31–32, 116
Clifford, Paul C., 72n.
Coefficient of displacement, 110–111
  computation of, 110, 112
  control of, 110–111, 113
Columbia University, Statistical Re-
    search Group, 1n., 7, 114, 121, 126n.,
    136n.
Combined variables and attribute plans,
    8, 19, 21, 69–70, 140–141
Continuous sampling inspection, 3
Control, meaning of, 98
  during production, 20–21, 75
  test for, 98
Control chart subgroup, 103, 105, 106
  number required to compute limits, 104
Control charts, in acceptance inspection,
    5, 9–10, 74–75, 99–102
  precautions for use, 102–103
  for averages, 103–105
  for coefficient of displacement, 110–
    111, 113
  for fraction defective, 109–110
  location of central line, 105–107, 111
  for number of defectives, 109
  for ranges, 106
  for standard deviations, 74–75, 106–
    107
  uses of, 98, 99, 109
Control limits, 98, 102
  for averages, 105
  for coefficient of displacement, 111–112
  for fraction defective, 109–110, 113
  for standard deviations, 107–109

Control limits, table of factors for, 197
Craig, C. C., 127n., 133
Curtailed inspection, 54, 56, 69, 70

D

d chart, 110–111, 113
Defective items, classification of, 41
  consequences of accepting, 40–42, 87
  replacement of, 29–31
Defects, listing of, 40, 86, 93
  per unit, 2, 20
Difference method, 150–151
Digits, dropping of, 143–144, 154
Distribution, flattened, 20–22
  non-central t, 122, 125–131, 133, 136,
    137
  non-normal, 18–21, 23
  normal (see Normal distribution)
  Poisson, 20
Dodge, Harold F., 7n., 72n., 121
Double-sampling plans, acceptance cri-
    teria for, 17–18, 57–59, 78, 95–96
  advantages of, 33–34
  calculation of risks, 122
  choice of, 18, 33–35, 47–48
  disadvantages of, 34

E

Error curve, 153, 154, 156
Error region, 154

F

Flattened distribution, 20–22

G

Grand lot, 61–62
Grand sample, 61–62
Grant, Eugene L., 98n.
Graphical methods, for acceptance cri-
    teria, 6, 60, 83–84, 153–156
  to test for normality, 22–23, 144
Grouping, of defects, 41
  of measurements, 21–22

I

Industrial Quality Control, 72n.
Inspection, amount of (see Amount of
    inspection)

Inspection, attribute, 2, 41, 70
  bias in, 145
  curtailed, 54, 56, 69, 70
  normal (see Normal inspection)
  reduced (see Reduced inspection)
  supervision of, 4, 22, 34, 51
  tightened (see Tightened inspection)
  types of, 2, 9–10
  variables, 1, 2, 5
Inspection level, 38
  choice of, 38–39, 43–45, 87, 94, 99–100
  in reduced inspection, 38, 67
Inspection lot, acceptance of, 10, 16, 17, 25, 29, 78, 101, 149–152
  in combined plans, 70
  in double sampling, 57–59, 78
  in graphical criteria, 154–156
  arrangement of, 52, 53
  definition of, 45
  disposition of, 10, 29–30
  formation of, 36, 45–46, 52, 88, 89, 94
  high-quality, 10, 11, 29, 43
  identification of, 52, 89
  low-quality, 10, 11, 25, 29–30, 43
  rejection of, 10, 17, 25, 29–30, 101, 154, 156
    in combined plans, 70
    in curtailed inspection, 69
    in double sampling, 57–59, 78, 150
    in graphical criteria, 154, 156
  resubmission of, 29–31, 68
  size of, 36–37, 45–46
  variation in quality of, 29, 36, 45–46, 72
Item of product, determination of, 40, 86, 93
  inspection of, 54, 89, 93, 94, 117

J

Jennett, W. J., 126n.
Johnson, N. L., 126n., 140, 141

K

Known standard deviation plans (see Known-sigma plans)
Known-sigma plans, advantages of, 73
  effect of inaccurate estimate of sigma, 75
  summary table of, double-sampling, 200–201
    single-sampling, 199

Known-sigma plans, table comparing AQL and LTPD with unknown-sigma plans, 202–203
  use of, 7–8, 72–74

L

List of symbols, 157–161
Lot (see Inspection lot)
Lot tolerance percent defective (LTPD), 28, 50, 76
  table of, for variables plans, 169

M

Match of plans, 76, 77, 116–121, 138
Mean, computation of, 55, 57, 58, 146
  control of, 103–105
  definition of, 14, 55
  effect of sampling error on, 104
  of grand sample, 62, 63, 92, 104
  as measure of lot quality, 3
Measurements, precision of, 21–22
  rounding off, 146
  tally of, 144–146
  translation (transformation) of, 95, 143–144, 150–151, 155
Multimodal distribution, 20–21

N

Navy, United States, 7, 50, 114, 117, 121
Non-central t distribution, 122, 125–131, 133, 136, 137
Non-normal distributions, 18–21, 23
Normal distribution, assumption of, 6, 14, 18–19, 22, 97, 125
  definition of, 18
  tests for, 22–24
Normal inspection, 38–39, 44, 65
  resumption of, 66–68, 123
  test for use of, 65, 79, 92–93
"Normal law" (see Normal distribution)

O

Operating characteristic (OC) curve, for combined variables and attribute plans, 70–71, 140–141
  computation of, 70–71, 76–77
  definition of, 25, 50

Operating characteristics (OC) curve,
        effect on, of value for k, 26–27
    of sample size, 27
    equation for, 125–132
    ideal, 27
    of single-sampling plans, 26
    table of, variables plans, 170–189
    for two-sided limits, 82, 85, 134–138
    use of, 25, 43, 50, 85
Operating characteristics, under known-
        sigma plans, 74–77
    match of, 76, 77, 116–121, 138
    with two-sided limits, 81, 82

P

p chart, 109–110
pn chart, 109
Peach, Paul, 72n.
Peaked distribution, 21
Pearson, Karl, 127n.
Percent defective, 10, 25, 41
    average, 30–32
    control of, 109, 110
    maximum, 31
    as measure of lot quality, 2, 3, 25–26,
        73, 136
    in terms of mean and standard devia-
        tion, 14–16, 110, 125, 133–134
    variation of, 29, 36
Poisson distribution, 20
Prime, use of, 157
Probability paper, 23
Process average, on an attribute basis, 63
    computation of, 61–63, 79
        frequency of, 61, 64
    in curtailed inspection, 69
    definition of, 61
    determination of, table for, 192–193
    in double sampling, 61, 96
    limits for, 65, 67, 79, 93, 124
        table of, known-sigma, 202–203
            unknown-sigma, 194–195
    number of items required, 61, 124
    use of, 60, 61, 64–66, 117
Proportion defective (see Percent defec-
        tive)
Proportional sample, 53, 145
Protection, in acceptance inspection, 24,
        37, 38, 43–44, 64
    in AOQL procedure, 31–32, 68

Protection, effect of sample size on, 36–37,
        46
    in known-sigma plans, 74, 75
    against low-quality inspection lots, 10,
        38–39, 44, 64–65
    with non-normal distribution, 23–24
    when process is in control, 101–102
        (See also Operating characteristic
        curve)
    against rejection of screened lots, 21, 70
Purchaser, use of term, 10–11

Q

Quadratic method, 151–155
Quality, of accepted product, 10, 11, 23,
        25, 29–32, 101
    control of, 9, 20–21, 75, 97–98
    evaluation of (see Process average)
    improvement of, 5, 29–30, 42–43, 66,
        99–100
    of item, 2, 3, 40–41
    of lot, 2–3, 25–26
    of sample, 11, 16, 25, 30
    of submitted product, 29, 38–39, 99–
        103, 121
        effect of, on choice of AQL, 41–42,
        100, 122–123
        (See also Average outgoing quality;
        Average outgoing-quality limit;
        Process average)
Quality specifications in relation to
        needs, 43

R

Receiver, use of term, 10–11
Rectangular distribution, 21
Reduced inspection, 38–39, 44, 65
    acceptable quality level for, 67
    when to use, 67, 74, 79, 123
Rejection (see Inspection lot, rejection
        of)
Rejection criteria, double-sampling, 17,
        57–58, 96, 150
Rejection region, 84, 154
Responsibility, division of, 50–51, 115
Returned lots (see Inspection lot, dis-
        position of)
Risks in sampling inspection, 4, 5, 11,
        16–17, 25, 38, 43

Rockwell hardness numbers, distribution of, 13–15, 145
Romig, Harry G., 7n., 121

S

Sample, drawing of, 48, 52–53
  inspection of, 2, 54, 69
  proportional, 53, 145
  random, 52–53
Sample size, 37–38
  classification of sampling plans by, 27
  combined variables and attribute plans, 70
  double-sampling plans, 17–18, 33, 121, 132
  effect of, on operating characteristics, 27, 44–45
  known-sigma plans, 7–8, 72–73, 76
  in relation to lot size, 36–37, 46
  variables plans, 4–5, 32–33, 117–118
  (See also Amount of inspection; Sample-size letter)
Sample-size letter, 37–38, 46–47
  in AOQL procedure, 68–69
  classification of sampling plans by, 27, 116
  determination of, 38, 46–47, 88, 94
  in reduced inspection, 38, 67
  table of, for AOQL and AQL classes, 196
  table for determining, 164
  in tightened inspection, 66
Sampling, choice of type, 18, 33–36, 47–48, 88, 94, 116–117
  double (see Double-sampling plans)
  "second chance" in, 33–34, 48
  rules for, 53
  types of, 3, 33, 34
Sampling error, 25, 43, 104
  effect of, on acceptance criteria, 16–17, 72
  of process average, 65
"Sampling Inspection," 1, 1n., 7, 32, 34, 35, 41, 114, 117, 122
Sampling inspection, continuous, 3
  lot-by-lot, 3
  objectives of, 10
  risks in, 4, 5, 11, 16–17, 25, 38, 43
  steps in, 4, 51
  uses of, 1

Sampling inspection plans, attribute, 1, 6–7, 32, 114, 121
  combined, 8, 21, 69–70
  selection of, 4
  variables (see Variables sampling plans)
Sampling inspection record, 148, 149
Screened lots, 8, 21, 22, 30, 68, 70
Screening, 9–11, 29, 30, 69
"Second chance" in double sampling, 33–34, 48
Sequential sampling plans, 3, 35, 122
  as alternative to variables plans, 34–36, 48
Sigma control chart, 74–75, 106–107
Skewed distribution, 19–20, 103–104, 144
Squared-difference method, 155–156
Standard deviation, computation of, 55, 57, 58, 105n., 106, 148, 151
  control of, 72, 74–75, 106–107
  definition of, 3, 13–14, 55
  effect of sampling error on, 107, 109
  of grand sample, 62, 63, 92
  of incoming product, 74–75, 107
  as measure of lot quality, 3
Standard sampling inspection procedure, attribute, 114–115
  composite, and variables, 116–117
  variables, 115–116
Statistical Research Group, Columbia University, 1n., 7, 114, 121, 126n., 136n.
Sublot, 52, 53
Supplement to the Journal of the Royal Statistical Society, 126n.
Supplier, use of term, 10–11
Symbols, list of, 157–161

T

Tallying measurements, 144–146
"Techniques of Statistical Analysis," 126, 136n.
Tightened inspection, 38–39, 65
  acceptable quality level for, 39, 66
  when to use, 65–66, 79, 123
Tolerance range, minimum, 81–82
Two-sided plans, use of, for known standard deviation, 80–82
  for unknown standard deviation, 82–84, 136–140
  use of two one-sided criteria in, 80–81, 85, 134–136

V

Variables inspection, definition of, 1, 2
Variables sampling inspection, advantages of, 4–5, 32–33
  disadvantages of, 5–6, 32
Variables sampling plans, 1–2, 4–6
  choice of, 24, 28–29, 48–50, 88–89, 122–123
  classification of, 27–28, 31–32, 116
  installation of, 50–51, 77, 116
  relation of, to attribute plans, 7, 47, 51
  scope of, 3–4
  summary table of, double-sampling, 166–167

Variables sampling plans, summary table of, single-sampling, 165
  table of, 170–189
Variation, causes of, 20, 21, 72, 97
  assignable, 97–98, 103
  inherent, 97–98
  control of, 101
Vendor, use of term, 10–11

W

Welch, B. L., 126n., 140, 141
Wolfowitz, J., 136n.

X

$\bar{x}$ charts, 103–105